MW00634319

Navigating the Insurance Maze

THE THERAPIST'S COMPLETE GUIDE TO WORKING
WITH INSURANCE – AND WHETHER YOU SHOULD

EIGHTH EDITION

By Barbara Griswold, LMFT

San Jose, California
www.theInsuranceMaze.com

Navigating the Insurance Maze: The Therapist's Complete Guide to Working with Insurance – And Whether You Should (Seventh Edition)
By Barbara Griswold, LMFT

© Eighth Edition, 2020
Seventh Edition, 2nd printing, October, 2018
Seventh Edition, First Printing April, 2018
Sixth Edition, 2015
Fifth Edition, 2014
Fourth Edition, 2013
Third Edition, 2011
Second Edition, 2008
First Edition, 2006

Published by Barbara Griswold, LMFT
San Jose, CA

Printed in the United States of America
www.theInsuranceMaze.com

All Rights Reserved. No part of this publication may be reproduced or transmitted in any form or by any means – graphic, electronic, or mechanical, including photocopying, recording, taping, or other information storage and retrieval systems – without the written permission of the author, except in the case of brief quotations embodied in critical articles or reviews.

This manual is intended to provide information to assist psychotherapists in different situations related to working with private insurance plans. It is not intended to address every situation that could potentially arise, and is not a substitute for independent legal, financial, or clinical advice or consultation. This manual attempts to give a general overview of private insurance plans. Some plans will not fit the descriptions herein. It is not intended as a manual for dealing with state or federal government plans such as Medicare or Medicaid, which may have different rules. Use of this manual does not substitute for reading individual provider or member contracts or provider manuals, or contacting the insurance company for information about a specific plan coverage, policies, or member's benefits. Be aware that the information given here may vary depending on situational factors, including the psychotherapist's license, state, plan type, and type and place of service. Thus, the reader should verify references or information contained herein.

ISBN: 978-0-9840027-5-7

Dedication
ଚ୨ ଔ

To all the underpaid therapists who work ethically and with integrity with insurance, despite the many challenges, barriers, frustrations, and all the ways that the system works against you.

To my patient and selfless husband, Doug, and my daughter, Maria.
I cherish you both more than you could know.
Thanks for tolerating all the time I spend staring at a computer screen or traveling away from home as I pursue my dreams. I hope I always make enough time for you.

And to my always-encouraging mom and dad,
who always told me I could achieve whatever I set my mind to.

Acknowledgments
ᵇᴿ Ⅎ

This book would not have been possible without Barbara Grover, LMFT, who was my co-presenter at my first public workshop on this topic. I cannot thank you enough for your consistent encouragement since then, and, more importantly, your friendship.

And for the generous contributions of their advice, time, and talents, I thank:
Susan Frager, LCSW, of Psych Administrative Partners, my billing advice guru;
David Jensen J.D., mental health attorney at CTSC Law;
Michael Griffin, J.D., LCSW, Staff Attorney at the California Association of Marriage and Family Therapists;
and
James Barrios and Lori Norr at BR Printers, who have patiently shepherded me through each edition of this book.

Most of all, I thank all of you with whom I have had the pleasure to correspond, consult, or meet at my workshops. I learn so much from you when you share your insurance stories, struggles and successes. You remind me daily how much I have to learn, which keeps me from getting too full of myself.

Table of Contents

≈⃝ ⃝≈

Introduction

ೞ ಲ

"A successful therapy practice is one where you don't need to take insurance."

This comment sums up how many therapists feel about working with insurance. We often see accepting insurance as equivalent to selling your soul to the devil, a sign of failure to make it on your own in private practice, or in the same way struggling actors see waiting tables: a way to earn income while making a name for ourselves.

I felt this way in 1990, when I opened my practice as a Licensed Marriage and Family Therapist and joined my first insurance provider network. I needed the referrals, and planned to resign when my practice was full. As I write this 30 years later, I am still a provider for more than 10 insurance networks and Employee Assistance Programs, despite the fact that I long ago reached my goal of a self-sustaining practice. Am I a masochist? Maybe. But I hope by the end of the book you will understand my reasons for staying.

As I talk to colleagues and workshop attendees on the subject of insurance, it has become clear that while we make our living in the health field, many of us are in the dark about basic facts about health insurance and reimbursement. This begs the question: Why is this topic -- which has such a significant effect on our practice and even the therapeutic relationship -- left out of the training of most mental health professionals?

Due to this lack of information, or perhaps because of fears, many therapists do not participate in insurance. In fact, a 2017 survey by the California Association of Marriage and Family Therapists showed that only 46 percent of their members had chosen were insurance network providers.[1] The American Psychological Association reports 30% of psychologists do not accept insurance.[2] Many clinicians have understandably been influenced by insurance horror stories. Fearing the compromise of confidentiality, loss of clinical control, micromanagement, increased paperwork, and discounted fees, many have chosen not to work with insurance. And those of us who do participate may feel we are stumbling along in the dark, making many costly mistakes, as we navigate the ethical, clinical, and administrative issues that come up as we put insurance into our practices.

This lack of a dialogue on the myths and realities of insurance is what led me to write this book. The goal of this manual is <u>not</u> to persuade you to accept insurance. It isn't right for everyone. My aim is to give practical information you didn't get in graduate school. Armed with facts instead of fears, I hope you'll be able to decide whether working with insurance is a wise idea for your practice. After all, this is one of the most important business decisions you will make as a therapist. And I see this as an area no therapist can avoid. We all have clients who seek insurance reimbursement, so it is important that we understand how insurance works, and what we need to do to help them seek reimbursement, as well as advocate on their behalf. Most importantly, even if you never sign an insurance contract, what you <u>don't</u> know <u>can</u> hurt you – and your clients.

I wrote this book because I am passionate about making the work we do accessible to people of all socio-economic backgrounds. Like you, I got into this profession to help others – not just the wealthy. Accepting insurance is one way to help clients from all walks of life to afford the vital services we provide. Also, in my mind there is something wrong with a system when clients -- who have often paid hefty insurance premiums -- can't use their insurance coverage to see the therapist of their choice.

1

Please don't overlook a few resources in the back of this book. There is a comprehensive glossary, so you can look up definitions to all those strange new words you come across. There is a listing of all the State Departments of Insurance so you can file complaints. There is a list of Resources to get more support with different topics. And there are all kinds of sample forms; if you'd like to purchase and download these forms to use in your practice, visit my website.

When reading the text, please keep in mind the book's limitations. First, while I will make many generalizations, remember that each insurance plan's policies may differ. Even within one insurance company, different accounts have different types of coverage. Second, the book's main focus is on working with private insurance plans. While many of the concepts and specific claim details are useful for working with any insurance plan, I do not claim to be an expert on government plans such as Medicare, Medi-Cal, Medicaid, Victim Witness/Victims of Crime, or insurance plans associating with the Veteran's Administration.

Writing and re-writing this manual (this is the eighth edition), leading workshops, and consulting with other therapists has been a humbling process: I continually learn how much I <u>don't</u> know. With any luck, after you are finished reading you will know what it has taken me 30 years to learn.

Barbara Griswold, LMFT

1

Why Take Insurance?

✂ ✂

As you traveled the long (it may have seemed unending) path toward licensure, perhaps you visualized your future psychotherapy practice. Maybe you dreamed of opening your own office. Of setting your own schedule. Of making a difference. Of having your own loyal and adoring clients. Most likely, you dreamed of a practice where each client paid your full fee out of pocket.

You probably didn't spend much time visualizing the business aspects of your future practice. Your training likely concentrated on the clinical, the theoretical, the legal and ethical sides of the field, but you probably never took a course on how to start, market, and maintain a small business. You may not even like to think of what you do as a business.

And that is why your visualization probably didn't include whether you'd take insurance. Perhaps you also heard stories from others that discouraged you from accepting insurance. The discounts. The paperwork. The limitations of coverage. The phone calls to check benefits and unsnarl claims problems. The need to discuss treatment decisions on occasion with case managers.

So Why Consider Accepting Insurance?

Private-pay is no longer the norm. Therapists continue to want to focus on developing a private-pay-only practice, despite the fact that the number of clients who pay out-of-pocket is surprisingly small, and declining. In fact, insurance was the most frequently used source of payment for health visits, with only 23 percent of these expenses paid out of pocket.[3]

▶ **The Affordable Care Act (the ACA, also known as "healthcare reform"), which went into effect in 2013, has meant millions more Americans have coverage or improved coverage for mental health care.** It may be harder to convince clients to forgo using their insurance, and to pay out of pocket for this care (for more on the ACA, see Page 36).

▶ **Insurance can be a great referral source.** When you become a provider for an insurance plan or Employee Assistance Program, you may be contacted by clients who were given your name by their plan, which can help fill empty therapy "slots." I get several calls each day from potential new clients who want to see someone on their plan. Due to my insurance participation, my practice is always full, with a waiting list. Now, this is not everyone's experience -- as they say, "your mileage may vary."

▶ **It may reduce your need for marketing and advertising.** The insurance plan will give out the name of participating providers to plan members who call asking for referrals, and list these provider's names on the insurance company website. If you hate advertising yourself, this is a nice benefit. You could think of your discounted rate as a prepaid marketing fee. "If you choose to let the insurance companies do the marketing, you will have more time to do therapy," says Casey Truffo, of BeAWealthyTherapist.net.[4] "Think of them as your sales staff. They work for you. You have basically hired them to do your marketing."

▶ **Insurance enables many clients to afford therapy.** With typical private-pay fees averaging $120 to $200 per session for a Master's level therapist, your services may be out of reach of much of the population. While clients may love you and value therapy, it is a harsh reality that some would have to choose between much-needed therapy and paying the rent. For them, paying full fee – or even a sliding scale fee – cannot compare to paying a $15 copayment. Accepting insurance is one way to make therapy affordable and accessible. For me, it also opens the door to see clients from diverse cultural and socioeconomic backgrounds.

▶ **Insurance may allow them to stay longer.** Even clients who can afford to pay privately for some therapy may be able to afford more treatment. I like to think of insurance as a type of subsidy or financial aid, which helps clients to partially finance ongoing treatment.

▶ **It's a way to attract the "therapy-avoidant."** Having insurance coverage brings in clients who might never have come to therapy. This is especially true of Employee Assistance Programs (EAPs), since they are a free employee benefit, and advertised at the workplace. It may give clients a "taste of therapy," and they often choose to continue on their own after the EAP sessions have run out (for more about EAPs, see Chapter 3).

▶ **Holding on to clients, old and new.** We've all had it happen – that client who switches insurance plans, and tearfully informs you she has to leave since you don't take her new insurance, and she can't afford to pay your fee. Or the new client who calls after hearing great things about you, but has to request a referral when he finds you don't accept his insurance. Accepting a variety of insurance plans avoids this loss – of clients and income.

▶ **Free training/resources.** Some insurance companies offer free or low-cost webinars, workshops, or teleconferences for their participating providers on a wide variety of clinical issues. Some even offer free Continuing Education Units. Many health plans put out regular provider newsletters, and post helpful online articles and resources for clients and providers.

▶ **Private practice can be isolating.** Believe it or not, sometimes it is helpful to have a case manager to discuss your client with, who might be able to help with treatment adjuncts, resources you didn't know about, or benefits you didn't know the client had.

▶ **My personal reason? Gratitude.** When I first saw a therapist, I was a full-time graduate student living on ramen and mac and cheese. It was insurance that allowed me to afford the psychotherapy that changed my life. Then seven years ago I was diagnosed with cancer, and insurance allowed me to get the hundreds of thousands of dollars of medical treatment that saved my life. Every day I am grateful for the wonderful doctors who accepted my insurance, and the opportunities insurance has given me. I hope to give others the same opportunities to get affordable treatment.

2

Understanding Insurance Plans
Decoding the Alphabet Soup

ೞ ೞ

There are few topics that stir such passionate feelings in the hearts of therapists as insurance. Much of this negative feeling is related to the frustration of trying to learn how to deal with a system which can be very confusing, especially to the newcomer. Also, the rules vary between insurance companies, and with each type of plan within a company, so it is nearly impossible to ever attain a feeling of competence.

To help you understand the types of insurance plans and the differences between them, it may help to use a case example.

Meet Jack

Jack comes to you at the urging of his wife, Jill. He reports he recently tripped over a pail of water and fell down a hill. Since the fall he has experienced recurring nightmares of the event, distressing recollections and flashbacks, hypervigilance, and has developed a phobic response when in the presence of a pail. Jack's anxiety has made it difficult to function in his job as a pail salesman at Pails "R" Us. Jack got your name from his insurance company, which we'll call CureQuick Insurance.

First, A Few Definitions

As Jack investigates his insurance coverage, he is faced with learning a new vocabulary. While I've included an extended glossary at the back of this book, let's start with some key concepts:

▶ **Deductible:** The dollar amount (usually yearly) that Jack has to pay for his medical expenses before his insurance begins to reimburse for expenses. Not all plans have deductibles. Some plans will waive Jack's deductible if he sees a network provider. During the deductible period, you bill the plan so the charge is credited toward Jack's deductible, but since you know the plan won't pay, you collect from Jack the contracted rate with the insurance plan. (Confused? We'll talk more about deductibles later).

▶ **Copayment:** The <u>fixed, flat fee </u>that Jack's plan may require him to pay for each visit (after the deductible is exhausted, if any). The plan pays the rest of the allowed amount.

▶ **Co-insurance:** In some plans, instead of a copayment, Jack pays some <u>percentage</u> of the provider's fee (after the deductible is exhausted, if any). Insurance pays the rest of the allowed amount. In rare cases, a plan will have both a copayment and a coinsurance.

▶ **Provider network/ panel:** These are the healthcare providers who have signed a contract with CureQuick to deliver services to Jack and other members of the CureQuick health plan. The providers usually agree to accept a fee discount and to file claims for the any CureQuick clients – this serves as an incentive for CureQuick clients to choose them.

Types of Mental Health Coverage

Jack is delighted to find out that Pails "R" Us has an Employee Assistance Program. This program entitles all employees and dependents to a certain number of free sessions yearly with a counselor in CureQuick Insurance's network

Employee Assistance Program (EAP)

An EAP is an employee benefit provided by some employers who have agreed to cover all employees and their dependents for a certain number of free counseling sessions per year (usually three to ten) with one of their EAP network providers. EAP therapists provide assessment, short-term counseling, and referral. An Employee Assistance Program is typically offered by the employer in addition to the employee's other mental health benefits. That is, clients might be eligible to use their free EAP sessions before they begin using their other mental health benefits. The EAP may be offered by the same insurance company that manages the mental health benefits, or another entity altogether. Not all employers offer EAP programs for their employees, so your clients may not have this benefit (for more on EAPs, see Chapter 3, "Employee Assistance Programs").

Jack gets a lot out of his EAP sessions, so is happy to learn that after the EAP sessions he also has ongoing mental health coverage through CureQuick Insurance. However, he learns that CureQuick has many types of health insurance plans, and Pails "R" Us offers more than one type of plan to employees. He can't recall which type he signed up for at enrollment time.

After his EAP sessions, Jack may one of several kinds of managed insurance plans.

What's a managed care plan? Back in what some therapists recall as "the good old days," insurance plans were mostly "indemnity" plans, or fee-for-service. These plans would indemnify -- or reimburse -- Jack or his providers for health care expenses as they were incurred. Jack was free to choose any provider he wanted to see, as often as he liked, and after he satisfied his deductible and paid his copayment, eligible services would be covered by his insurance plan.

However, as health care costs rose each year, insurance companies responded by changing the structure of health plans. These new "managed care" plans reduced costs in a variety of ways, including setting yearly session or spending limits, signing contracts with preferred providers willing to accept discounts, and requiring pre-authorization (pre-treatment approval from the insurance company) and treatment review.

What types of insurance plans are there? It would be impossible to list all insurance plan varieties and details, so only the most common types are outlined here.

1. **Health Maintenance Organization (HMO):** An HMO typically covers a higher degree of preventive care than other plans, in order to minimize later care costs. Jack chooses or is assigned a primary care physician (PCP) who coordinates his care and may make referrals to specialists (though typically Jack would not need a referral to see a therapist). An HMO may have central medical clinics, or it may contract with a network of individual practitioners in the community. HMOs usually offer broader coverage and lower out-of-pocket expenses for the client than other plans. However, many clients don't realize that an HMO will only cover visits to network providers, and their care may undergo more scrutiny than with other plans. For the client, it may represent lower copayments, but be the least flexible health plan in terms of provider choice.

2. **Preferred Provider Organization (PPO):** With a PPO, the insurance company will cover Jack's visits both to network providers and out-of-network providers, with higher benefits paid when he visits network providers. If he chooses a network provider, Jack will usually pay much less than if he goes out of network, typically only a copayment, and the provider will file claims on his behalf. When Jack chooses to go to an out-of-network provider, he will usually have to pay the provider in full at the time of service, and later can submit an invoice to the insurance plan to get some portion reimbursed. However, PPOs may involve deductibles and larger coinsurance amounts than HMOs. The provider's treatment is less frequently reviewed by the plan, and authorizations aren't usually needed.

3. **Exclusive Provider Organization (EPO):** An EPO is like an EPO/HMO hybrid. Like an HMO, the insurance company will only cover Jack's visits to local network providers, though EPOs may have smaller networks. However, like PPOs, he shouldn't need an assigned PCP to coordinate care. Also, Jack will get the benefit of paying only a copayment at sessions, a participating provider discount during the deductible period, and the provider will file claims. In addition, like a PPO, Jack typically won't need preauthorization. EPOs and HMOs usually have lower premiums but may have higher deductibles.

4. **Point-of-Service Plan (POS):** Another HMO/PPO hybrid, this plan offers a great deal of flexibility and choice. With a typical POS plan, Jack would have a two- or three-tiered plan, and could choose any of the benefit levels when seeking care. He could choose a therapist from Tier 1, which would allow him to choose any therapist on CureQuick's HMO panel, and then the plan would operate just like a normal HMO. He may instead obtain treatment from any participating provider in Tier 2, CureQuick's PPO network, and in this case the plan would then work like a normal PPO. Finally, he may have a third tier, permitting him to go outside of both networks, and be reimbursed when he sees an out-of-network provider. If he chooses Tiers 1 or 2, Jack will get the benefit of a participating provider discount, and the provider will file claims. Each tier typically represents higher out-of-pocket expenses for Jack than the one before it.

Confused? Let's put the different plans side by side and on the next page and compare them.

A Comparison of Typical Insurance Plans

	Are Out-of-Network Providers Covered?	Client's Usual Cost For Service	Who Files Claims?	Treatment Pre-Authorization Required?
EAP	No	Free, paid for by employer	Provider	Yes
HMO	No	Typically lowest copayments, may have no deductible	Provider	Sometimes, but depends on plan
PPO	Yes, but at a higher cost to the client	Usually deductible, lower costs for client when s/he sees network providers, higher costs for out-of-network providers	Provider, if in-network; client generally does if visiting an out-of-network provider	Typically not
EPO	No	Typically has deductible and copayment	Provider	Typically not
POS	Yes, but at a higher cost to the client	Lowest costs for clients when they see HMO providers, higher for PPO providers, highest for out-of-network providers	Provider, if in-network; client generally does if visiting an out-of-network provider	May be needed if using HMO provider

Note: Plans vary greatly. Please consult the specific health care policy or contract for plan details.

Making Choices That Fit Your Practice

Hopefully you can see that as a therapist you have a lot of choice about how involved to get with insurance. Having said that, it is important to note that when you become a network provider, the insurance company will typically want you to provide services for all their members, regardless of their plan (HMO, PPO, etc.), though EAPs are often handled separately.

Your first decision will be whether to become a network provider, or to accept insurance as an out-of-network therapist, or some combination of these two options (though remember, not all plans cover out-of-network providers). Let's review.

If You are a Network (Panel) Provider:

- ▶ **Pros:** This should bring new client referrals from the insurance company and their website which may reduce your need for marketing. You'll be able to retain clients who have insurance and can't afford to pay privately.
- ▶ **Cons:** You must sign a contract with the plan. You accept a discounted rate for services, and must bill the insurance plan yourself. You may not "balance-bill" the client -- that is, you cannot bill your client for the difference between your full fee and the insurance plan's discounted fee, as you agreed to this rate when you signed the contract. Treatment may need to be pre-authorized and can be reviewed by the plan.

If You are an Out-of-Network Provider:

All providers who have not signed a contract with the insurance plan are considered out-of-network providers. You don't need to do anything to become an out-of-network provider.

- ▶ **Pros:** You don't have to sign any contract with the insurance plan. You do not have to discount your fee. Clients can pay you in full and you can simply give them an invoice -- also known as a "Superbill"-- to submit themselves to the insurance plan (see Sample Invoice on Page 145). Your treatment will not need to be pre-authorized.
- ▶ **Cons:** You won't get client referrals from the insurance company – you'll need to market your practice. Clients may leave you (or not come to you) and instead find a network provider on their plan, since this may be substantially less expensive for them.

It's important to keep in mind that <u>whenever a bill is submitted by you or your client to an insurance plan, your treatment is subject to review, whether or not you are a network provider</u> (more about this on Page 48).

The chart on the following page is another way of looking at your choices. It outlines the choices of two therapists who have selected different involvement levels with insurance, and how those decisions work for them.

A Tale of Two Therapists: Two Extremes of Provider Participation

In our example below, Doug has decided he doesn't want to join any provider networks. He wants to avoid the paperwork and discounts he knows are part of the insurance world, so he chooses to be an out-of-network provider only. Maria, however, has chosen to join a few networks, hoping to fill those empty slots in her practice. She is willing to do some paperwork and take discounts in exchange for the referrals. I do, however, caution providers to be careful not to join too many panels -- if all your clients are insurance clients, all your slots are discounted.

	Doug Out-of-Network Provider only	**Maria** Network Provider for Some Plans
Can Accept What Insurance Plans?	▶PPO out-of-network (if license is covered by plan) ▶POS out-of-network (if license is covered by plan)	▶ EAP ▶ HMO ▶ PPO ▶ POS ▶ EPO
How Much Can Therapist Charge?	Therapist's full fee	Agrees to accept discounted contract rate accepted when she joined plan. <u>Cannot</u> bill clients to make up for any fee discount
Amount of Paperwork	Typically minimal, may only involve giving client invoice/superbill (see Sample Invoice on Page 145)	Depends on company. Once accepted on panel, paperwork may include filing claims, keeping track of payments and unpaid claims, and occasional appeal letter to fight claim denial
Must Therapist Submit Claims?	No. Client pays full fee and therapist gives client an invoice or superbill to submit to the plan (see Sample Invoice Page 145)	Yes
Will Insurance Refer Clients?	No	Yes, directly (phone) and indirectly (via online provider directories)

Tax-Advantaged Savings Accounts; HSAs, MSAs, HRAs, and FSAs

As employers look for new ways to share the burden of rising health costs with their employees, new types of plans have emerged. Some employers offer these instead of (or in addition to) more traditional health plans.

1. **Health Savings Accounts (HSA) or Medical Savings Accounts (MSA):** Many employers offer employees a health savings account, which allows the employee to set aside pre-tax dollars from their income for future medical expenses.  Contributions to the account can be made by your client, his employer, or both. If Jack had an HSA, he would be given choices on how to invest these funds, and then can use the funds to reimburse his qualified health expenses during the year. It's as if Jack put aside money in a piggy bank throughout the year and then when it came time to pay a healthcare provider, he could pay himself back out of this piggy bank. Except in this case, if he chose to save the money for future health expenses, the account would grow through investment earnings.

   Jack would need to be enrolled in a high-deductible health plan and he could have no other major insurance coverage. The funds can roll over from year to year and are portable. He could take them with him if he changed jobs, changed medical coverage, became unemployed, or moved.

   HSAs and MSAs allow a lot of choice, including how much to put in the account, what expenses to pay out of it, and what investments to make. Jack could even use the funds to pay for approved health expenses his insurance doesn't cover (such as for over-the-counter medications or bandages), or save the money for future health needs. And because of the high deductible, Jack may have a very low premium.

   Perhaps the most attractive benefit of all? The account provides Jack with triple tax savings: deductions when he contributes to the account, tax-free earnings through investment, and tax-free withdrawals for qualified medical expenses.

   Some clients will ask their therapist for an invoice for any paid amounts so they can submit it to their HSA or MSA for reimbursement. Other plans allow clients to use the money in their accounts to reimburse providers directly for their portion of the costs. Clients may have access to these accounts via debit cards, so you could be reimbursed in this way. To accept the debit card in your practice, you may need to be registered as a healthcare provider with your credit card processing company. With some plans if you are a participating provider with the health plan operating the HSA or MSA you would submit a claim as if it was a regular insurance plan, and the provider is simply paid directly out of the member's account. Check with the health plan in advance for instructions.

2. **Health Reimbursement Arrangements (HRA)**: Very similar to an HSA account. The main difference between an HRA and an HSA is that HRA funds are provided only by an employer for an employee.

3. **Flexible Spending Accounts (FSA):** This account allows for reimbursement of childcare, dependent care, and/or health care expenses, and enables employees to pay for these expenses with a non-taxed portion of their salary. The main difference between an FSA and an HSA is that FSA funds typically must be used within the calendar year or they are forfeited. Therefore, if Jack guesses he will be paying about $2000 in the coming year for childcare and medical expenses, he will have his employer deduct this amount from his salary over the course of that year. His employer would deposit these pre-tax payroll deductions into his (non-interest-bearing) FSA. Anytime Jack submits an invoice from a medical or child-care provider, he would be reimbursed with funds from his account.

A client with an FSA does not need a high-deductible insurance plan. As with MSAs, some clients will ask their therapist for an invoice for any paid amounts so they can submit it to their FSA for reimbursement. Other plans allow clients to use the money in their accounts to reimburse providers directly for their portion of the costs -- clients may have access to these accounts via checks or debit cards, so you could be reimbursed in this way. As was mentioned earlier, to accept the debit card in your practice, you may need to be registered as a healthcare provider with your credit card processing company.

3

Employee Assistance Programs

ઠજ ંલ

As mentioned in the previous chapter, an Employee Assistance Program (EAP) is a benefit provided by many employers who cover their employees and dependents for a certain number of free counseling sessions per year (usually three to ten) with one of their EAP network providers. EAP therapists provide assessment, short-term counseling, and referral.

Studies have shown that by offering this program to workers, employers can minimize absences, improve productivity, and in other ways contain the employer's cost of employee stress and other mental health issues. In one study, 66% of all employees entering the EAP program reported having moderate, severe, or extremely severe problems with stress, anxiety or depression. Three months after completing the EAP sessions, less than 32% fell into these same categories.[5]

An Employee Assistance Program is in addition to (and usually separate from) other mental health coverage the client might have through their medical insurance. Clients usually use their free EAP sessions before they access their other mental health benefits.

Jack's employer may have an internal EAP, in which the EAP counseling office is located at the workplace, and the EAP therapists are on the company payroll. Or the EAP may be external, made up of a network of community providers. In Jack's case, Pails "R" Us has hired the CureQuick network of providers to provide both the EAP and ongoing mental health insurance for its employees. Sometimes the same insurance plan will provide both EAP and mental health sessions; in other cases, a separate EAP firm may provide EAP services.

It is unfortunate that not everyone has an Employee Assistance Program. It is also unfortunate that clients who <u>do</u> have this benefit often aren't aware of it. You could ask the client's health insurance plan when you call, but if the EAP plan is handled by a separate firm, the plan may not be aware of the EAP coverage. Particularly for clients concerned about therapy cost, you might suggest that the client talk to his employer's Human Resources department or check his benefits manual.

The EAP plan may offer other types of assistance, such as free legal, financial, or tax consultation, eldercare or childcare referral assistance, educational and career support and referrals. However, these visits may count against the client's total number of allotted EAP sessions.

When a client uses an EAP, it is important to keep in mind:

▶ **Pre-authorization is always needed.** The client will need to call the EAP to get this.

▶ **There is no "out-of-network" EAP option.** Clients must see a participating EAP provider.

▶ **EAP sessions are free.**

▶ **EAP sessions are available for the employee, spouse, domestic partners, dependents, and often for anyone else who lives with the employee.** Each can receive their own EAP sessions for unrelated issues.

▶ **Sessions are typically very limited in number (usually 3-6).** Some EAPs only allow this set number per year. However, if there is a new presenting issue that comes up, some EAPs will allow you to count this as a separate event, and grant additional sessions. And some occupations offer unlimited EAP sessions (such as some fire and police departments).

▶ **Sessions are confidential.** EAP clients often worry that what they share will be shared with their employers. This is not the case: Only statistical information (such as how many employees used the EAP, what types of issues were dealt with, and how many reported progress) might be revealed. Some additional information may be shared if counseling is mandated by the workplace or court (for more on confidentiality, see Chapter 15).

▶ **Sessions don't need to be work-related.** Any topic is OK.

▶ **No diagnosis of mental illness is necessary.** Clients do not need to have a diagnosis. This is not typically the case with other types of mental health coverage. In addition, the sessions don't need to be "medically necessary" (more on this in Chapter 9).

▶ **Your role as an EAP provider is to provide assessment, referral, and brief problem resolution.** One insurance plan put it this way: "EAP providers are most effective when they think of themselves as the early architects of a member's recovery rather than the means to that recovery."[6] Another said "EAP counseling is typically present-centered and does not seek extensive exploration or attempted resolution of long-term family of origin issues."[7] So be sure to set realistic goals and treatment plans within the given time frame. If the client continues in therapy past the EAP sessions, goals can be modified at that time.

▶ **But the EAP provider may wear many hats.** EAP therapists also assist employers by providing Critical Incident Stress Debriefings (CISD), consultations to employers, mandated employer and employee trainings (e.g. sexual harassment or chemical dependency), employee wellness/mental health seminars, and by representing the EAP at employee health fairs and orientations.

▶ **Follow-up may be expected.** As an EAP provider you may be expected to follow-up with clients after the EAP sessions are over. Document any follow-up (or attempts) in the client's record. You may also be expected to fill out a case closure form for the EAP when you are done.

Questions and Answers

I'm confused. Sometimes the letters "EAP" seems to be used to refer to the Employee Assistance Program itself. At other times, it seems to refer to the counselor working in the program.

Right. EAP may stand for "Employee Assistance Program" or it may refer to "Employee Assistance Professional," or "Employee Assistance Provider," the title of the clinician providing the services for the Employee Assistance Program. You have to figure it out from context.

Can anyone apply to become an EAP provider?

It depends on the network. Some plans are simply looking for licensed providers. Others would like to find those who can demonstrate experience in assessment, short-term problem resolution counseling, and referral. They typically want to see good brief therapy and crisis intervention skills, and chemical dependency assessment experience is a plus. However, many Employee Assistance Programs now require EAP experience or special certification before they will put you on their "sub-network" of EAP providers. This makes getting your foot in the door more of a problem. One health plan for example, stated they required either active status as a Certified Employee Assistance Professional (CEAP), or two years of verifiable experience as an internal EAP counselor or as an external EAP consultant to other organizations.[8] In addition, they require advanced training, certification, or work experience in the assessment and treatment of substance abuse. Another plan stated they required CEAP status or "1,500 hours of combined training and experience that resulted in expertise in the following areas: addiction counseling, job-related issues/performance improvement, short–term counseling, family and relationship counseling, assessment and referral."[9] But don't despair, other plans don't share these requirements.

Can I negotiate my rate before joining the EAP?

Sometimes, yes. I've been successful several times in getting a higher rate from an EAP due to my experience providing Critical Stress Incident Debriefings (CISD), Employee Wellness Seminars, and Employer-Mandated Trainings, like Sexual Harassment and Substance Abuse. They said this qualified me for their "expert" contract (for other ideas on what to highlight in your pursuit of a raise, see Raises, Page 118). Humana EAP states on their website that "we may be able to designate you as an experienced EAP provider if you 1) hold a certified employee assistance professional (CEAP) credential, 2) are an employee assistance specialist, 3) hold EAS-C certification, 3) have at least 2 years of experience routinely providing EAP services. Providers designated as an experienced EAP provider may get preference in EAP referrals."[10]

Why was my client referred directly to her insurance for treatment, rather than her EAP?

When your client contacted the EAP plan, the EAP intake counselor may have felt that your client's problem would need longer-term treatment than could be provided in the EAP sessions, so referred the client directly to use her insurance plan's covered mental health sessions. This may include clients with suicidal or homicidal ideation, severe or chronic mental illness, active substance abuse, or the need for immediate or more long-term treatment.

Can I just bill the insurance plan for EAP sessions as I would for any other insurance session?

This depends on the plan. In my experience, most EAPs have their own claim forms which they'll often send with the authorization, or you'll need to download. You will sometimes be asked to wait to bill for sessions until all EAP sessions are completed. You may need to attach a closed case form which summarizes treatment -- many companies will not pay without these forms. Some

EAPs allow you to use a CMS-1500 claim form (more about this in Chapter 11) to bill for EAP sessions, but some plans may require you to use a different CPT code for EAP sessions (more on CPT codes in Chapter 11). As always, ask the plan. It is wise to bill EAP sessions on a separate claim than any regular insurance sessions to avoid confusion.

Will Employee Assistance Programs pay for missed appointments or late-cancelled sessions?

Usually not, but check your contract. One plan I work with will pay for missed sessions. One pays $25 for the first missed session. Some will allow you to deduct a session from the client's total EAP benefit for each missed session. Some will not allow you even to bill the client for the missed session. Others allow you to bill the client if the client has previously agreed (in writing) to pay for missed sessions.

What if Jack needs further treatment when his EAP sessions end?

One of the following scenarios is possible for Jack:

1. **Jack's CureQuick EAP sessions may be all the mental health coverage he has.** In this case, you will have to refer him to appropriate and affordable community resources, or, if allowed by the EAP, it may be possible to continue to see him in your private-pay practice (see next question below).
2. **Jack may have further mental health benefits, also handled by CureQuick.** You might then refer him to a CureQuick network therapist, possibly even yourself, if the EAP allows self-referral.
3. **Jack may have further mental health benefits, handled by another insurance company.** You might then refer him to a therapist within the other company's network, possibly even yourself, or Jack could forgo using that other insurance to continue to see you, if the EAP allows self-referral.

So, Jack can continue working privately with me after the EAP sessions are over?

Most insurance companies have no problem with self-referral. Treatment must, of course, be within the scope of your competence and practice, and it's a good idea to give alternate referrals (in writing). However, some EAP plans do not allow self-referral: They do not want referral decisions to appear clouded by a therapist's desire to fill an empty therapy slot in his or her practice. The guidelines of the Employee Assistance Professionals Association state that "any actual or perceived conflict of interest among EAP professionals and service providers shall be avoided."[11] Contact the EAP plan to ask their policy or check your contact.

Even EAPs that do not allow self-referral may make exceptions in certain situations, including:
1. Continuity of treatment would enable successful and most rapid closure of clinical issues.
2. Disruption of service with you might place the client at risk.
3. You are working on an issue in which you possess an unusual expertise.
4. There are no available participating network providers in the same geographic area.

The private-pay agreement: If Jack wants to continue to see you (and your EAP contract allows self-referral), it is a good idea to have him sign a private-pay agreement (a Sample Private Pay Agreement is on Page 159). This agreement states that he understands his therapy is no longer covered by the EAP or insurance, and he is now responsible for paying your full fee (or one that you have negotiated with him). Signing this type of agreement protects you from having Jack come back later, saying he didn't understand his sessions would no longer be covered by the plan.

What about management referrals, also known as mandatory or supervisor referrals?

Managers and human resources personnel can formally refer employees whose problems are affecting the workplace or work performance. These referrals require special handling, even if they involve voluntary attendance by the employee. An employee may not be able to return to work and may be on unpaid leave until he reports to an EAP counselor or completes treatment.

Contrary to popular belief, in most cases the EAP counselor is <u>not</u> typically expected to contact the supervisor or employer directly. In my experience, attendance and/or progress information is given only to the case manager at the EAP plan. What will the case manager tell the client's supervisor? A typical policy is articulated by Beacon Health Options EAP in their Participant Statement of Understanding for mandatory referrals: "You will be asked to sign an Authorization to Disclose Information for Formal or Mandatory Referrals to the EAP. With this authorization, the following non-clinical information will be provided to your supervisor or another designated worksite representative: 1. Whether or not you have followed through in contacting the EAP; 2. Whether or not treatment has been recommended; and 3. Whether or not you are participating in and complying with your treatment plan. 4. Other information as you designate. Your supervisor will not be given clinical information about the specifics of your problems. Note: Your employer may take disciplinary action based on the information provided or based on your refusal to release information."[12]

Even though the client may understand that in these cases the sharing of information is a condition of treatment, it is a good idea to discuss the types of information you are being asked to release, and to whom you will be releasing it, and have the client complete your own release of information before making any disclosures.

If a client discusses harassment issues, worker's compensation, company wrongdoing, or legal action, this may limit their confidentiality. It is advised that you get legal consultation and talk to the client about these confidentiality issues, and talk to the case manager at the EAP program before making recommendations to the client about pursuing litigation or filing complaints against the employer or insurance company. Remember that if there is litigation your charts could be requested, so document mandated cases particularly carefully.

What if Jack asks me to write a letter excusing him from work? What if I am asked to fill out disability paperwork or fitness-for-duty determinations?

The EAP is not a medical service, staffed by medical providers who could fill out disability paperwork or determine if an employee is fit for duty. In general, you should avoid any verbal or written correspondence with the client's employer regarding the client's ability to work or any other aspect of treatment. This is usually outside the scope of your work as an EAP, particularly, and is better left for the client's doctor or psychiatrist.

If the client moves from EAP sessions to non-EAP sessions within the same health plan, can I submit a claim for both types of sessions on the same form?

As was mentioned, many EAPs require their own claim form, so you may not be able to use the same form for both EAP and routine mental health sessions. Also, EAP claims may need to be sent to a different claims address than regular mental health claims, even if being processed by the same plan.

4

Horror Stories: Myth or Reality?

ಋ ಞ

When therapists explain why they have chosen not to accept insurance, it often becomes clear that their decision was based (at least in part) on misinformation or myths. Let's explore some myths about getting involved with insurance:

<u>Myth?</u> "If I take insurance, I'll have to do billing, and lots of paperwork.

<u>The facts:</u> There's no denying that insurance involves paperwork. How much depends on your choices. If you loathe the idea of billing, you can choose to remain an out-of-network provider, collect your full fee, and provide an invoice or superbill that the client can submit to the insurance plan (see Sample Invoice Page 145). Or, if you want referrals but less paperwork, you might join just a few plans. Another option would be to only join plans that require minimal provider paperwork. A final alternative would be to hire a billing service to handle the paperwork for you (more about Billing Services on Page 89).

<u>Myth?</u> "If I take insurance, I'll have to discount my fee."

<u>The facts:</u> Should you choose to become a participating provider, there is no getting around it — the reduced fee is by far the biggest complaint of most panel therapists. But some therapists feel it may be worth taking the discount for the referrals -- a discounted fee may be better than an empty therapy slot -- and for the other reasons outlined in Chapter 1.

<u>Myth?</u> "If I take insurance, I'll have to do brief therapy, and sessions will be limited."

<u>The facts:</u> It is true that insurance plans are looking for therapists who are skilled in brief therapy. And it is true that in the past, most plans had yearly session limitations. However, <u>due to the Patient Protection and Affordable Care Act (healthcare reform) and federal parity laws, most plans now must allow unlimited sessions for mental health for all diagnoses covered by the plan</u>, if the sessions are deemed to be medically necessary. In my own practice, I can cite examples where plans have covered treatment that lasted decades for clients with chronic mental illnesses (for more on parity laws, see Page 31; the Affordable Care Act, see Page 36; and medical necessity, see Page 48).

Myth? "If I take insurance, my therapy will be micro-managed by idiots at the insurance companies."

The facts: While in the past case managers were often unlicensed clerks, these days reviewers are usually licensed Master's-level clinicians. In my experience, while these clinicians will occasionally call to discuss cases, this happens mostly for more complex, lengthy, or chronic cases. And such treatment reviews are probably rarer than most therapists imagine. In over 29 years I have only been reviewed a handful of times, and I have never felt micro-managed. Most plans do not make routine requests to view treatment plans, and if reviewed my requests for more sessions are typically approved. Though plans must offer unlimited sessions since federal parity laws took effect in 2010, they can declare the sessions "not medically necessary." Therefore, plans seem to be doing more medical necessity reviews in order to control costs (see Page 48 for more on this).

Myth? "All the networks are full."

The facts: While it is true that in many geographical areas many insurance panels say they are full, they make exceptions every day, accepting new applicants if they need someone with certain skills, experience, language abilities, location, or because they need to diversify their panel in some way. It is unpredictable, so you should always apply, and keep applying (for more about joining plans, see Chapter 5). Even those plans that are full today have changing needs. The plan may land a new employer account in your area tomorrow, and be scrambling to dig through their files for resumes from providers in your area who have previously expressed interest.

Myth? "If I take insurance, my clients will have to get a doctor referral to see me."

The facts: Long ago, a doctor referral was required by many insurance plans, so this impression persists. However, times have changed, and almost all plans now allow client self-referral -- no doctor referral required. Even if they require pre-authorization, this is usually something the client or provider can get over the phone from the health plan, without a doctor referral.

Myth? "If I take insurance, I'll have to give diagnoses to clients who aren't mentally ill."

The facts: While it is true that health insurance only covers mental illness, most clients are covered for adjustment disorders and other non-severe mental illnesses. Also, employee assistance programs don't require diagnoses. Remember, it is insurance fraud to give a diagnosis where none exists. If you cannot justify a diagnosis, the client should be told that you cannot in good faith bill the medical insurance plan, and the client can always choose to pay out of pocket. Do not fall into the trap of giving all your clients the same diagnosis, one you feel can't hurt them. This is fraud (more on diagnosis and fraud, Page 100).

Myth? "If I take insurance, I'll have to deal with HIPAA."

The facts: Accepting insurance does _not_ automatically mean you become a "covered entity" under the Health Insurance Portability and Accountability Act (HIPAA), or that you have to comply with the requirements of HIPAA. Most lawyers interpret HIPAA to only apply to you if you will be communicating any confidential client Protected Health Information (PHI) electronically -- via the Internet -- or if you have someone else conducting these transactions electronically on your behalf. However, there are good reasons why all therapists should become knowledgeable about and compliant with HIPAA regulations. For more information about HIPAA, see Chapter 7.

5

Becoming a Network Provider
Selling Yourself to Insurance Companies

౭౦ ౪౮

I like to say that in the "good old days," all you needed to join a provider network was a pulse. While that may be an exaggeration, when I joined my first panels in 1990, many panels required little more than an application and resume. Those days are gone. In most well-populated areas of the country, if a network isn't full, insurance companies can afford to be choosy, in part because there are more therapists applying.

Since it is expensive to develop and maintain a provider network and database, it is in a plan's best interest to maintain the fewest possible providers on their network. However, plans are required to maintain minimum "density standards" (the required number of providers in any given region). They also must meet the varied clinical needs of their members in your area.

So, let's say you have decided to join a provider panel. Where do you start?

> ▶ **Get a list of insurance companies** that may cover your services. Your professional organization or state Department of Insurance (DOI) may have a list of insurance companies that operate in your area, with contact numbers and addresses.

> ▶ **Ask colleagues what provider panels they belong to**, and about their experiences with each plan, and for contact information.

> ▶ **Call each insurance plan, or go to the plan's website to apply.** On the phone, ask for Provider Relations, Provider Contracting or Network Development. If the network is "closed," this means the plan is (allegedly) not accepting new providers in your area. But don't take no for an answer – plans will always make exceptions. Ask about plan needs, and sell yourself. If you have a needed specialty, have an office in a less populated area, see children and adolescents, treat veterans, specialize in substance abuse, treat ADD/autism, can see clients on weekends, or can conduct sessions in another language, let them know — they might make an exception for you (see Page 23 for a list of what they are looking for).

▶ **Don't apply without an amazing resume to sell you.** I suggest you send a letter of interest and targeted "insurance resume" to sell yourself to the plan, asking for an application (for more on what to include in this letter and resume, see the following sections).

> _**Tip:** If you are not accepted, don't give up. Eventually, perhaps through attrition, there will be openings on the panel. Every three to six months, resubmit a letter of interest with your insurance resume. Try to target your letter to a specific person, or, failing that, to "Manager, Network Development" or "Manager, Provider Relations." Try to follow-up by phone or e-mail, and if possible speak to your target person._

▶ **Keep a communication log** with dates of your contacts, names of the people you spoke with, their responses, and action taken. I'd advise separate files on each plan.

▶ **While most insurance companies will NOT accept unlicensed therapists** as network providers (in fact, many require that you have been licensed two to three years), some plans may reimburse you or even accept you on the plan if you have very unique skills, or languages, or are in an underserved location. So, ask around or call and ask the plan. Also try smaller and regional plans or employee assistance plans.

▶ **Consider forming a group.** Panels like the idea of contracting with provider groups, when possible. A provider group is usually defined as a group of providers who share the same billing Tax ID, and a unified billing process.

Why You Should Have an "Insurance Resume"

Because plans can afford to be picky when accepting new providers, your resume may be the most important tool you have for telling them about yourself. But chances are your current resume may not be the best sales tool, and may even contain things that could jeopardize your acceptance. I strongly urge you to prepare an "insurance resume," to give you an edge when applying, and to highlight the experience and training you have that plans are looking for. I recommend a resume that:

▶ **Begins with a summary (in bullet form) of your specialties and qualifications** that would be attractive to an insurance plan; See the list on next page for ideas of things to highlight
▶ **Includes a list of places of employment,** job titles, job descriptions, degrees, licenses, professional affiliations, and relevant lectures given or groups facilitated, impressive specialized trainings received, and publications/articles written.
▶ **Is brief, with a two-page maximum.** Since insurers are flooded with resumes, they are unlikely to read a long resume, and the best info might get buried.
▶ **Helps you stand out.** You need to think about how you are different from the therapist in the next office, and make that clear.
▶ **Contains those all-important insurance buzzwords,** such as "symptom-reduction focus," "problem-solving therapy" and "cognitive-behavioral treatment."

The problem is most therapists are not great at selling themselves. So, get help with writing this (if you need help writing your insurance resume, see "Mental Health Insurance Consultants" listed in Resources, Page 133).

What to Include in Your Letter of Interest and Resume

When applying, write a one page letter of interest to include with your resume. Request to become a provider on their behavioral health network, then summarize your qualifications. It is OK to duplicate things said on your resume. You might highlight these topics in both your letter and resume, and pick information that shows you in the best light.

- **Specialties/training**: What skills set you apart from colleagues? These may include working with eating disorders, children, ADD/autism, veterans and military families, PTSD/trauma, EMDR, gay and lesbian issues, transgender.
- **Telehealth:** Let them know if you provide telehealth, and that this can help you serve their members throughout your state, including underserved areas.
- **Brief therapy/crisis intervention** training and treatment experience
- **Substance abuse** training, assessment, and treatment experience and codependency
- **Insurance/EAP experience**: Mention the number of years of experience as an insurance/EAP provider, or your familiarity with insurance expectations.
- **Location:** Highlight if you have multiple offices, or if you're in an underserved area
- **Availability:** e.g. large number of open hours available for members, or at times when other therapists traditionally are not, such as weekends and/or evenings
- **Current members:** Mention if you see a large number of the plan's members as an out-of-network provider (it may save them money to make you a network provider)
- **Language:** Can you conduct therapy in another language? Sign-language?
- **Ethnic/cultural diversity**: Insurance plans seek therapists that represent diverse genders, races, ethnicities, and cultures. Cross-cultural competency is also valued.
- **Coordination of care**: Mention your hospital privileges, willingness to treat clients in the hospital or after discharge, and if you work closely with physicians and other treating providers, or experience working on a multi-disciplinary treatment team
- **Groups/Classes:** Let them know if you offer therapy/support groups, or psycho-educational classes (though they may not cover the latter). You could include a flier from a group or workshop you are leading.
- **Treatment plans:** Your experience with behavioral treatment plans, relapse prevention plans and discharge plans
- **Set up for electronic billing** (may be required by the plans).

Panel Applications

So, you are finally sent an application, or fill one out online. Now what will you be asked? It varies with the plan, but it may include:

- **Theoretical orientation:** Insurers may ask you to describe your theoretical orientation, and often provide a checklist. Most insurance companies are looking for therapists competent in short-term therapy, cognitive-behavioral treatment, and crisis intervention. This doesn't mean you should lie, but keep in mind if you identify yourself as only "psychodynamic" or "psychoanalytic," you could be making yourself less desirable to them.

- **Percentage of cases ended in 5, 10, 15, 20+ sessions:** Again, while they understand you'll have longer term cases, they are looking for therapists who are able to provide short-term, problem-focused treatment. They'll typically want to see most treatment ending in less than 20 sessions. It's OK to guesstimate, though you might want to start keeping records.

▶ **Your availability.** Plans are looking for providers who will have enough openings for their members, so may not accept you if work very part time. Sell them on your evening or weekend availability. If you work very part time, try to sell them on your specialties. Plans have similar availability standards, typically looking for therapists who can schedule routine appointments for new clients within ten business days, and, for current clients, looking for non-life-threatening emergency cases to be handled within six hours, urgent cases within 48 hours, and 24/7 access to a live person or answering machine, able to refer clients in life-threatening emergencies to crisis services.[13]   The plan may check up on this by contacting you periodically to check availability, or by asking clients how long they waited for a session.

▶ **After-hours/vacation coverage:** Many companies require some form of 24-hour coverage for your clients. They also may want your outgoing answering machine message to instruct clients on how to reach you (or a covering therapist) in an emergency or to direct them to go to a nearby emergency room or dial 911.

▶ **Documents:** Applications typically will ask you to attach a copy of your license, malpractice insurance (they may have certain coverage minimums), and to list your Continuing Education Units from the past few years.

▶ **Your friends.** They may ask for professional organizations you belong to, the names of psychiatrists you refer to, and colleagues who can vouch for you.

▶ **Any history of trouble.** They may ask about past malpractice claims, or if you've ever had your license, privileges, or professional membership revoked. If you have, you may need to submit legal documents to show settlements and dispositions.

▶ **They may ask you to sign a release** to allow them to check out information you've given, about your degrees, malpractice, references, licensing, etc.

▶ **They may ask you if you have a CAQH number.** CAQH ProView is a free, centralized, standard online profile form, where providers are able to enter very detailed practice information for health plans to view. The goal is to reduce duplicative paperwork that would need to be submitted at each plan. While not all insurance plans use CAQH, it is recommended that you go the CAQH website, register, and get a CAQH number. Filling out the online profile can take up to two hours the first time, but can save time in the long run. It can give plans more information about you when considering your application. To be clear: CAQH is not an insurance plan, nor is it a job board -- you still have to apply to the health plans. Think of it as a private online file cabinet that, with your permission, health plans can use to see your file if they want to learn more about you. The downside: You will routinely be asked to visit the site to upload your latest documents and keep your information current.

▶ **If the application you receive includes a provider contract**, this doesn't mean you have been accepted yet. *Read it carefully.* Legal jargon isn't easy to understand, so call the plan with questions. It may be possible to negotiate a contract provision or even fees before joining (especially if you speak a second language). Be sure you understand what you'll be paid before you sign this contract. Watch out for special provisions. One EAP program may allow you to continue privately with a client after sessions are exhausted, but only at the discounted fee. Another may state that you cannot continue to see a client after EAP sessions end. In my practice, I created a quick-reference spreadsheet, with notes about each plan's contact info, rates for each type of session and different provider policies, to avoid accidently breaching the contract. Keep a separate file for each plan.

► **Go over the application thoroughly before submitting.** Even a complete application can take six months to process -- you don't want to leave anything out.

Single Case Agreements and Transition of Care Agreements

A Single Case Agreement (SCA) means that for one client only, an out-of-network therapist is treated as a network therapist. This is typically done only in special situations, such as when there is a change of insurance during treatment, when there is no network therapist with appropriate qualifications available (or within reasonable driving distance of the client), or when all available professionals have some type of dual role. It may also be used when the provider is going through the credentialing process. I've done SCAs when I left a network, and the plan I left continued to pay me to see a client -- but I was able to negotiate a higher negotiated rate.

If Jack's insurance changes, and you are not a network provider for his new plan, you may be able to receive a certain number of "Transition of Care" (TOC) sessions from the new plan. The idea is that the new plan agrees to cover a certain number of sessions while Jack is transitioned to a network provider at the new plan. However, Jack may choose to just use these TOC sessions and then pay you out of pocket if he chooses to continue with you.

Usually Jack will need to be the one to make the Single Case Agreement or TOC request to his new plan. A case manager from the plan will need to approve the request, and you'll need to fill out some paperwork to agree to a fee and to abide by plan policies. You will need to collect the client's copayment and submit claims for this client. Sometimes you may be able to receive a reimbursement rate that is higher than the network rate, or even your full fee, so don't be afraid to ask for more than you are offered.

Unfortunately, such temporary network status rarely becomes permanent, except where you fill a deficit in the network. Before you pursue this option, you may want to see if he has out-of-network benefits, and explore the pros and cons of going this route instead.

Questions and Answers

What kind of reimbursement can I expect?

Ah! This is probably the most common question I am asked, yet it is one of the most difficult to answer. It's important to remember that network providers -- even ones on the same plan -- may be paid very different amounts for the same service. It is also difficult to answer because as independent contractors with the insurance plan, providers are generally discouraged from discussing their reimbursement rates with other therapists due to anti-trust issues (for more on anti-trust, see Page 119). Reimbursement varies (often wildly) depending on insurance company, the provider location city/state, license, the service billed for, and whether the provider has ever negotiated a raise. It is best to call the plan and give them the particulars of your situation and ask for their reimbursement rate before joining.

Can I negotiate my fee or anything in the contract before joining?

It's rare but not impossible. Provider contracts and fee structures are fairly standard, and most plans won't negotiate them up front, but a few times Unless you have something insurers might be willing to pay extra for (e.g., some valuable specialty, skill, language fluency, or if they are in need of providers in your area), it is unlikely they will raise your rates before they have had a chance to evaluate your performance, or get client feedback. However, other than potentially delaying your application, it can't hurt to try! I've been successful twice in getting a higher fee from the start (for more on Raises, see Page 118).

How long does it usually take for them to process my application?

It varies greatly between companies, but the wait can sometimes be three to nine months.

Once I am accepted, am I in for good?

Usually. Insurance companies will require that you go through what's called the recredentialing process every two or three years. You'll usually just need to update your practice information, malpractice, license, etc. and they will also review information in your provider file, including any member complaints, and statistics on client satisfaction and length of average client treatment, often broken down by diagnosis.

While filling out recredentialing paperwork is a hassle, if you don't do it in a timely manner, you may be dropped from the network. Many plans have now contracted with third-party Credentialing Verification Organizations (CVOs), such as CAQH ProView or Aperture. As was described earlier, CAQH allows you to complete a single provider profile online to meet the credentialing needs of multiple insurance plans. Once you submit your practice data, participating plans no longer need to contact you directly with recredentialing forms to seek the necessary information. You will then just need to update your information regularly with CAQH.

Should I pay a fee to join?

Application fees are rare, and should be cause for caution. I've never paid a fee. Many therapists I know paid fees to join a plan and never received referrals. If you are considering a network that charges a fee, ask about other providers' experience with that plan. It is recommended that you do some investigation to find out if the company is actually providing insurance coverage to clients, or just creating and selling a list of providers.

I see clients in my home office. Is this okay?

Some insurance companies accept home offices, but others won't. If they do, they will typically have a long list of requirements. The office, client entrance, waiting area, and client restroom may need to be separate from the residence common space, used only for business, and you may need dedicated office phone/fax lines. Clinicians may be required to notify clients in advance that the office is in the home, warn of pets, inform clients if there is no waiting room. Telephone screening may be required prior to the first appointment, and high-risk or potentially violent clients may not be allowed to be seen in a home office.[14]

If you have a telehealth-only practice, and do all your telehealth services out of your home, this also may or may not be allowed by insurance plans. You'll need to check with each insurance plan you work with to see if this is allowed.

6

Talking to the Insurance Plan
Who to Talk To, How to Get Through

ༀ ༁

How do you know who to call for what? The hierarchy and titles vary with the company, but let's take a minute to review the relevant "cast list" at an average insurance company.

Administrative Staff

▶ **Provider Relations:** Deals with all provider-related questions. May handle applications, recredentialing, provider information changes, reimbursement rate increase requests, and other administrative duties.

▶ **Customer Service:** Don't be fooled by the title — these folks can be very helpful to providers. While not clinicians, they can handle most non-clinical issues, including answering your basic questions about a client's benefits, coverage, and claims.

▶ **Claims Department**: Handles all claim-related issues, such as unpaid claims, adjustments, claim denials, overpayments, and underpayments.

Clinical Staff

▶ **Intake Worker**: Since outpatient therapy clients are typically self-referred, most won't deal with an intake worker. But EAPs may require the client to contact an intake worker to get pre-authorization. The intake worker takes basic clinical information about the presenting problem, assesses for risk factors, makes referrals to appropriate network providers, and gives initial authorizations.

▶ **Case Manager/Care Manager**: Case managers handle treatment reviews, evaluate the therapist's requests for additional sessions, and advise therapists on clinical issues that arise during treatment. There may be a case management team that handles all calls relating to members from a specific employer.

► **Clinical Director/Medical Director:** Advises the case management team on high-risk or difficult cases and proposed denials or member complaints. Develops policies and guidelines for the company. It is rare that you'd interact with them, except in clinical crises, to request an exception to plan policies, or to appeal a care manager's denial.

► **Appeals Department:** If your request for additional treatment or your claim is denied, and you appeal, these are the folks who will review your appeal.

Navigating the Automated Phone System

It isn't always easy to get through to the right person at an insurance company. In fact, it isn't always easy to get through to a person at all. But here are some tips to keep in mind:

► **What time is it there?** Make sure you call during normal business hours in the time zone of the insurance company's headquarters. If you are located on the West Coast, this may mean calling before 1:00 or 1:30 pm. (Note: it's best to avoid busy days like Mondays and even Tuesdays). After normal business hours you may reach a recorded message. Even if you reach a live person, after-hours staff may have limited ability to help, and only be able to assist with clinical emergencies and referrals.

► **Allow yourself enough time to make the call.** Five or ten minutes between clients is typically not enough to unsnarl a claim or authorization problem. Running out of time and having to call back will only add to your frustration.

► **Before you dial, take a deep breath.** Get all your paperwork together. Be ready to give the client's name, date of birth, insurance identification number and group number, Social Security Number, as well as your name, phone number, and Tax ID number (your Social Security Number or Employer ID Number) and National Provider ID number (NPI), if you have one. If you are calling about a claim, know the claim ID, the date(s) of service, and full amount you charged.

► **Formulate your question or problem and desired outcome concisely,** so you can be routed to the correct person. Be patient and friendly.

► **Leaving a message?** Leave as much identifying information as possible. This may include your name, phone number with area code (repeated), the client's name (spelled out), the insured's name, plan ID number, client's date of birth, the date(s) of service in question, the charged amount (if it is a claim issue), and details about your problem. If leaving clinical details, be specific.

A sample message follows:

"Hi, this is Ima Great MFT. That's I-M-A G-R-E-A-T calling from San Jose, CA. My number is 408-555-1234. That's 408-555-1234. I'm calling about my client Jack Klutz, K-L-U-T-Z, ID# NCF0045672, birth date 2/1/61. I'm calling about Claim #24563242 for date of service 5/7/20, total billed amount $150. I was told when I called to check coverage on 5/1/20 (Call confirmation #42543) that the client did not have a deductible, but when the claim was processed the charges went toward her deductible. Can you please look into this and get back to me?"

Tip: **Want to talk to a live person?** If you reach the insurance company's automated service (e.g. "for the status of a submitted claim, press 1, for claims address, press 2"), but you would rather speak to someone with a pulse, you can often interrupt and say "Customer Service," "Representative," "Associate," or "Agent" -- <u>even if these options are not mentioned.</u> If all else fails, follow the prompts for a while, and then try the voice commands mentioned above. Or press "O" or say "Operator. You can also do nothing in response to all prompts, and you will usually be transferred to a live person (they need to have this for those with rotary phones).

▶ **Don't take the "automated benefits" or "fax back" option.** The automated voice may offer to give you an automated (recorded) summary of benefits, or to fax you a summary of the client's benefits. Avoid this offer in favor of speaking to a live person, when possible. All the answers you need are typically not covered in these summaries. Also, the summaries may have only information about medical coverage, not mental health, so they can be quite misleading.

▶ **Document the call.** Many insurance companies document all calls, and may even tape record them, which can be good for you if you later need proof they gave you incorrect information. But you should also document the name (first name and last name initial) and when possible the direct phone number or extension of each person you speak to, and a record of exactly what they told you.

▶ **Or forgo the phone altogether.** Plans want you to go online whenever possible. While I strongly recommend that you call when initially checking insurance benefits, a lot of follow-up information may be available via the insurance plan's website or multi-payer portals such as Availity (ex. claim status, claim payment details, authorization confirmation, etc.). You might be surprised that sometimes you can even get answers from company staff via email, which is usually best for general questions about company policies. (For more about Availity and what you can do at the company website, see Chapter 14.)

7

Parity, HIPAA, & Healthcare Reform
Legal Junk You Need to Know

Just seeing the word "law" or "regulation" might make you break out in an itchy rash, and make you decide to skip this chapter. But don't. Unless you've been living under a rock, you know that in the last few years there have been sweeping and historic insurance laws that are changing the way the whole system operates. But in more detail, here are three important laws that therapists need to know about that may affect how you operate your practice -- and potentially help your clients.

Parity Laws

In 2010, federal parity legislation went into effect that was a true game-changer, improving the coverage of millions of clients, and bringing many changes for clients.

First, a little history. Historically, insurance covered medical illnesses only. When plans did start covering mental illness, clients seeking therapy typically had higher copayments and deductibles and more limited sessions for therapy visits vs. medical visits. However, as evidence emerged for the biological basis of many mental illnesses, many states enacted regulations requiring insurance plans to provide coverage for mental illness that was "at parity with" (equal to) the coverage for medical diseases covered by the plan. This typically meant the insurance plans had to provide the same visit limits, deductibles, and copayments for mental health visits as for medical visits. But it is very patchwork: Some states have no state parity laws. In some, parity is granted to all diagnoses. In some states, parity is limited to certain diagnoses considered biologically-based (also called Severe Mental Illnesses, or SMI). For example, under California's state law, for example, only the following diagnoses are afforded parity coverage: Schizophrenia, schizoaffective disorder, major depressive disorders, obsessive-compulsive disorder, bipolar disorder, anorexia nervosa and bulimia nervosa, panic disorder, pervasive developmental disorder, and certain serious emotional disturbances of a child.[15]

What changed in 2010? In 2010 the Mental Health Parity and Addiction Equity Act (MHPAEA) of 2008 went into effect. This federal Act stated that health plans regulated by the Act could no longer impose limits on inpatient or outpatient mental health visits if no such limit existed in the client's coverage for medical visits. Plans could no longer have higher deductibles or copayments for mental health or substance abuse. In addition, if a plan reimbursed when a client went out of network for medical care, it also had to offer out-of-network coverage for mental health.

How did the Parity Act change things for clients? The Parity Act affected over 100 million people in large group, state-regulated plans, and Medicaid programs. For most clients, it gave them better insurance coverage for mental health and substance abuse treatment. Most now were eligible for unlimited sessions, no matter what their diagnosis, when before they may have had annual limits unless they had a serious diagnosis (there is a catch -- see below). Some clients now had a lower deductible and/or copayment for their sessions. Some clients now had out-of-network coverage.

The fine print? The MHPAEA does not require a plan to cover all therapists, all licenses, or all diagnoses -- it says only that if a mental health or substance abuse diagnosis and service is covered for medical providers, it needs to be covered for mental health providers. And while the Affordable Care Act requires all plans purchased through State health exchanges and individual plans to comply with the requirements of the Parity Act, there are some plans (most notably some small employer groups and self-insured plans) that don't have to abide by the MHPAEA. Also, the Parity Act doesn't require "good" coverage: A client may still have coverage limitations and/or a high deductible or copayment, if their medical coverage does.

And there's a bigger catch. While most plans must now offer unlimited therapy sessions, they retain the right to cover only visits they consider "medically necessary." This makes treatment reviews by a member of the insurance plan's clinical staff one of the few options they have for limiting treatment. Unfortunately, medical necessity criteria are defined by the plan and fairly subjective. Some plans have started to ask therapists – *even out-of-network therapists* -- to periodically undergo treatment reviews or complete written treatment updates to track treatment goals, progress, necessity, and effectiveness. For this reason, I strongly suggest all therapists (even those who never sign a plan contract) become versed in the language of medical necessity and get the plan's medical necessity criteria (for more on Medical Necessity, see Page 48).

What if this Act doesn't cover my client? If you call the plan, and they tell you a client has a limited number of sessions per year, chances are the plan is not covered by the Parity Act-- it is probably a self-insured/self-funded or ERISA plan. Self-insured plans do not have to follow federal regulations. In this case, your state parity law may come into play. In many states (such as California, as was described earlier), equal coverage is limited to clients with certain diagnoses deemed "Severe Mental Illness (SMI) or "Biologically-Based" disorders. In these states, there are two levels of coverage -- one for clients who have one of the diagnoses listed in the state's parity law, and another level of coverage for clients with "non-parity diagnoses." Because states vary on which diagnosis are considered parity diagnoses, you will need to know your state's parity law so you can get accurate coverage information when checking a client's insurance. If the insurance plan rep says there are session limits, ask if this is a self-insured plan, and ask if there are different levels of coverage for parity and non-parity diagnoses. If the plan rep doesn't recognize the word "parity," try "Serious Mental Illness" (SMI), "Severe Emotional Disturbances" (SED), or "Biologically-Based disorders." For more assistance, contact your professional association, your state's Department of Insurance (see Appendix A, Page 129), or the parity resources listed in the Resources List of this manual (see Resources, Page 133).

HIPAA: The Health Insurance Portability and Accountability Act

[Author's note: The following section is intended as a general overview of complex regulations. There are many interpretations of HIPAA which will differ, and understanding will no doubt evolve over time with legal clarifications and challenges. For more information, refer to the Endnotes on Page 125 and the HIPAA section of Resources on Page 133.]

One of the most confusing issues for therapists is whether they need to comply with HIPAA. The Health Insurance Portability and Accountability Act was signed into law in 1996. The Act was passed in large part based on concerns about the privacy of medical information in light of the increasing use of computers by insurance plans and medical practices. It was also designed to streamline the electronic exchange of client information, to reduce fraud, and to minimize a client's chance of losing health insurance coverage when he or she is no longer covered by an employer's health plan.

HIPAA has four main parts that HIPAA providers need to become informed about:

1. **Privacy Standards:** Describes how a client's Private Health Information (PHI) may be used and disclosed
2. **Electronic Transaction and Code Set Standards:** Creates a universal "language" for reimbursement used by all insurance plans (ex. diagnosis and procedure codes).
3. **Security Standards:** Outlines how to safeguard confidential information from loss, theft, hacking, tampering, etc.
4. **National Identifier Requirement:** Requires all HIPAA providers to have a universal identification number, the National Provider Identifier (NPI), instead of using different provider numbers for each health plan.

Do I have to deal with HIPAA regulations?

It's a good idea. But the Act states that only HIPAA "covered entities" are required to follow HIPAA's regulations. You are a covered entity if you are a health care provider, health care plan, billing service, or clearinghouse *that conducts specific transactions via the internet*. According to David Jensen, a mental health specialty attorney at CTSC Law:

You **DO NOT** have to deal with HIPAA if you exchange all client health data with insurance plans by mail, phone, or fax -- not via e-mail or Internet. Common examples:

1. You have a private-pay-only practice, and don't deal at all with insurance claims
2. You give invoices to clients to submit to insurance (see Sample Invoice, Page 145)
3. You bill insurance, but ONLY submit paper claims by mail or fax <u>and</u> you have no one submitting electronically on your behalf (ex. a billing service or clearinghouse)

You **MUST** deal with HIPAA regulations if you exchange any client information with a health plan <u>electronically</u> (via e-mail or Internet), such as:

- Submitting claims, inquiring about a claim, or receiving a response via internet
- Inquiring about eligibility, coverage, or benefits, or receiving a response online
- Requesting a treatment or referral authorization, or receiving a response online
- Receiving an electronic Explanation of Benefits (EOB) or remittance advice online
- Having a billing service or claims clearinghouse do any of the above on your behalf.[16]

HIPAA Questions and Answers

I contact clients via e-mail, or schedule appointments online. Am I a "covered entity?"

No. In these cases, the client is acting on behalf of himself. HIPAA only applies when you disclose a client's private health information to a third party like a health plan -- your client is not a third party.

Are interns, associates and trainees covered by HIPAA?

Yes, it applies to all health care providers, defined as "any person, business, or agency that furnishes bills or receives payment for health care in the normal course of their business."

What about notes? I hear HIPAA requires me to keep two different sets of notes.

Not so. Michael Griffin, staff attorney for the California Association of Marriage and Family Therapists, says "HIPAA speaks of two types of notes. The first type is **progress notes**, which are part of the medical record. These are factual notes kept about the sessions (including topics discussed, treatment plans, dates of service, and recommendations made). Progress notes would also include medications, session start and stop times, the type of service provided, results of clinical tests, diagnoses, prognosis, and progress."[17] (For more on progress notes and what should be in yours, see Page 54).

The second type is **psychotherapy notes** – sometimes called "process notes." These are an optional record you may keep of your feelings, thoughts, ideas, reactions, and analysis of sessions. HIPAA affords these notes more protection. "Therapists should not have to release these to a third party or to an insurance plan for an audit or evaluation. These should be kept separate from the progress notes, but some lawyers have interpreted HIPAA to say that you may keep these notes in the same chart as long as there is some divider," says Griffin.

OK, so if I'm a "covered entity," what do I need to do to comply with HIPAA?

It's probably easier than you think. While it is not within the scope of this manual to cover all the details of complying with HIPAA, here are a few things you'll need to do:

- ► **Learn about HIPAA.** Take a HIPAA compliance course or read a compliance manual.

- ► **Give all present and future clients a copy of the HIPAA "Notice of Privacy Policies."** This Notice outlines HIPAA confidentiality rights. Do not alter the policies; just add your contact information, name, address, etc. You will need to give a copy to ALL clients from now on, even to private-pay clients. (You can get a sample Privacy Notice from your professional association, a HIPAA course, or in my Practice Forms Package -- see Page 133 for more info).

- ► **Have clients sign an acknowledgement saying they have received your Privacy Policies.** A sample form may be available from your professional organization. Or you can simply incorporate the necessary wording into your Treatment Agreement (more about treatment agreements on Page 44; see Sample Treatment Agreement Page 143).

- ► **If clients have objections** about the Privacy Policies, provide them with the necessary forms where they can express objections and ask for exceptions (again, these forms are available from professional organizations or any HIPAA course or manual).

- ► **Follow HIPAA security rules.** Provide computer security, including virus protection, backup, firewalls, and passwords. Shred old confidential records, lock file cabinets and offices, and limit access. If you want to exchange confidential client information by fax, you will need a dedicated fax machine (one that is not used also as a phone line) in an area that is only accessible by authorized persons.

► **Apply for a National Provider Identifier, or NPI.** The NPI is a provider number that is unique to you, and used by all health plans in their communication with you. HIPAA-covered entities must use the NPI in all electronic transactions The NPI is free and easy to obtain. The NPI does not replace the need to use your Tax I.D. number on claims -- either your Social Security Number (SSN) or Employer Identification Number (EIN) is still required for tax reporting purposes (for more on the EIN, see Page 66, Box 25, or about getting an EIN or NPI, see Resources, Page 133).

► While only HIPAA-covered-entities are required to get a NPI, any health care provider may obtain one -- applying does not automatically make you a covered entity. However, soon NPIs will likely be mandatory. Health plans are urging all providers to get one -- some are even requiring new providers to have one.

► Billing services and clearinghouses you work with should use your NPI on your claims/invoices. Therapists who are employed by clinics or agencies should use the organization's NPI in one part of the claim, but may also need to get their own NPI for the box that requests "treating provider's NPI" (more about this in Chapter 11).

Is HIPAA being enforced?

Oh, yes. In 2019 alone, the U.S. Department of Health and Human Services Office for Civil Rights received 29,853 complaints of HIPAA violations. All of these were reviewed: 19,584 were resolved after intake and review, and 9,825 either required technical assistance or corrective action by the provider.[18] In 2019, the most common complaints were:
1. Impermissible uses and disclosures of a client's protected health information (PHI)
2. Lack of safeguards of protected health information
3. Lack of patient access to their health information
4. Lack of administrative safeguards of electronic protected health information
5. Use / disclosure of more than the minimum necessary protected health information.[19]

A word about the "Minimum Necessary" Standard: This HIPAA standard allows providers to use, disclose and request only that amount of a client's protected health information (PHI) that is reasonably necessary to accomplish the task. You can get in trouble for releasing more information than necessary. In some situations, you are allowed to release more than the minimum, such as when exchanging information with another provider for treatment purposes, when a client has signed a release, and when it is required by law, such as mandatory child, elder, or dependent adult abuse reporting.

But hasn't HIPAA enforcement been waived?

I know, confusing, right? In March, 2020, the Office of Civil Rights (OCR) sent out a notification that during the COVID-19 pandemic national emergency, HIPAA covered entities could provide telehealth services through telehealth platforms like Skype or Facetime that don't fully comply with the requirements of HIPAA Rules. The notice said that OCR "will not impose penalties for noncompliance with the regulatory requirements under the HIPAA Rules against covered health care providers in connection with the good faith provision of telehealth during the COVID-19 nationwide public health emergency."[20] However, this notification focused only on the provision of telehealth through platforms that are not HIPAA-compatible. It does not relieve you of the other HIPAA responsibilities discussed in this chapter. (For more on Telehealth, see _____)

For more information on HIPAA, and how to apply for a NPI, see Resources on Page 133.

Health Care Reform: The Affordable Care Act (ACA)

In March of 2010, President Obama signed the Patient Protection and Affordable Care Act into law, often referred to as "ACA," "health care reform," or "Obamacare." This Act set up a multi-year phase-in of sweeping changes in the health industry, with the goal of insuring all 33 million uninsured Americans, and making care more affordable. While ACA provisions are constantly being assailed in Congress, some highlights of the ACA's original provisions:

- ▶ **U.S. citizens and legal residents were required to obtain basic health insurance,** or pay a fee to help offset the costs of caring for uninsured Americans, (unless a member of an exempt religious group or waived due to financial hardship)

- ▶ **Plans were required to cover young adults under 26,** even if married, living outside the home, eligible to enroll in their employer's plan, or financially independent

- ▶ **Medicaid was expanded in many states,** allowing more clients to qualify

- ▶ **State-based "exchanges" -- also called marketplaces -- were created,** through which individuals and small businesses can purchase coverage, often with the help of a government subsidy. Similar to travel websites which allow consumers to compare airline flight prices to the same destinations, the exchange showed consumers their insurance coverage choices and costs, all in one online website. Exchange shoppers can choose from different coverage levels, and different insurance plans

- ▶ **Plans could no longer refuse to sell or renew policies to -- or charge higher premiums for -- adults or children with pre-existing health conditions** (except for tobacco use).

- ▶ **Plans could no longer charge women more,** or discriminate based on sexual orientation

- ▶ **No annual or lifetime dollar limits were allowed on most covered benefits**

- ▶ **Plans now had to offer a minimum benefit package, including mental health and substance abuse coverage,** and certain free preventive services, including depression screening (and contraceptives, except for plans with religious exemptions)

- ▶ **Parity was extended to plans offered by the state exchanges** (see Parity, Page 31)

What has the ACA meant for therapists? It's obvious that now that millions more clients have insurance, more clients are looking for network providers, and it can be hard to convince clients to pay privately for their treatment. Thus, many providers who never considered working with insurance are giving it a second thought. Also, many clients (and therapists in private practice) who are not covered by an employer health plan can purchase insurance through their state's exchange.

To get the most current information about Healthcare Reform, see www.healthcare.gov.

8

Starting Therapy
Checking Coverage and Intake Sessions
ജ രൂ

You run a victory lap around the sand tray after learning your CureQuick application has been accepted. At work, Jack breaks begins crying when he sees a pail in the men's room, and a coworker urges him to get help. He finds his insurance card, calls CureQuick, and finds out he has coverage for therapy.

First Contact

How does Jack come to be your client?

► **Jack may find your name on CureQuick's website,** where the participating provider list is posted (note: be sure to keep your online provider profiles updated once accepted). Or perhaps he gets your name from CureQuick, after calling to request a therapy referral. Of course, Jack may also come to you via one of your normal referral sources (colleagues, former clients, friends, his physician, etc.).

► Jack will likely research you on the internet. According to Hitwise, 68% of new patients begin their search for a medical provider with a search engine.[21] Add to this the number that get your name from their online insurance plan directory or another source, and then visit your website, and you'll see why it is *essential* to have a dynamic, informative website that will attract potential clients. If given your name and several others, and you have no website, clients are likely to go to the next name on the list.

► **Jack calls (or e-mails) for an appointment.** While you may do initial contact by e-mails, I like to talk briefly by phone before the first appointment (this reduces the likelihood of a no-show). Also, I recommend that you <u>ask Jack for his insurance information during this phone call</u> (I'll explain why later in this chapter).

▶ **Pre-authorization (pre-treatment approval) is usually not required, but check.** If so, Jack will need to obtain an authorization number from CureQuick before the first session. Have him call you back with this number before you meet. <u>Most plans do not allow providers to bill clients for a session when the provider failed to obtain a required authorization.</u>

▶ **Just "passing through"?** Instead of needing pre-authorization, Jack may be allowed a certain number of "pass-through" sessions per year. This means that he can refer himself to therapy for a certain number of sessions. After this, you would need to contact the insurance company to get approval for further treatment.

▶ **Not a provider for Jack's insurance plan?** Call the plan and check to see if he has coverage for out-of-network providers. In some cases, Jack may only have a slightly higher out-of-pocket expense to see an out-of-network provider, and he may be willing to pay this difference if he wants to see you. Watch out for those often-high out of network deductibles, though.

<u>Why You Should Contact the Plan – Before the First Session</u>

I can't stress enough how important it is to contact a client's insurance up front – ideally even <u>before</u> the first session. This is vital if you are a network provider, less important if you are an out-of-network provider. Many therapists do not check coverage, feeling (understandably) that it is the client's responsibility. It's tempting to let the client handle this, since it is time-consuming, and clients may appear knowledgeable about their benefits. But while it might be a hassle to check their benefits, if you don't you are increasing the possibility of a claim denial, lengthy phone calls to investigate and fight the denial, potential time writing appeal letters, clients upset by treatment disruptions, and therapy bills that clients may be unable to pay.

▶ **During your first contact with Jack,** after setting up an appointment, tell him you would like to check his insurance benefits in advance "to be sure there is no problem down the line." Clients are typically thrilled that you are willing to deal with their insurance on their behalf. Then get the necessary insurance information from Jack over the phone or via secure e-mail (see Page 41 for a form to use when checking coverage).

▶ **If you don't call now, you may not get paid.** If you don't check coverage up front, it may take months before you find out that your claim was denied, or that charges went toward the client's deductible. You also may find that for some reason you are not a covered provider with his plan. For a variety of reasons, this could leave an unpaid balance of hundreds of dollars. Even if your contract allows you to bill Jack, he might be unable to pay, or he may have left your practice, making it hard to collect.

▶ **Don't assume.** You may think since you have other Pails "R" Us or CureQuick clients that you already know the coverage details. But every account may be different -- coverage depends on which CureQuick plan(s) Pails "R" Us bought for its employees, and which plan Jack chose. Also, plan benefits may change yearly.

▶ **Don't trust the information on Jack's insurance card.** Why not? See Page 45.

▶ **Doesn't a call to Jack's insurance plan breach confidentiality?"** Some therapists worry because the client hasn't really even become a client or signed a release to allow this call. However, this type of communication is typically permitted by law -- but do check in your state. California Civil Code, for example, states that even without a release, medical information "may be disclosed to an insurer...or employee benefit plan...to the extent necessary to allow responsibility for payment to be determined and payment to be made."[22]

▶ **Don't believe anything your client tells you about his coverage.** He is often misinformed or not aware of recent benefit changes. And after reading this manual you will have a much more detailed list of questions to ask to find out what services will be covered, at what rate, and with what limitations.

▶ **"Can't I get coverage information by going online?"** Many plans have websites that enable you to check benefits, deductibles, etc. But often this information is incomplete or out of date, and may not answer important questions such as how much of a deductible has been used this year, telehealth benefits, required codes/modifiers, and mental health claims address. Also, when you call, plans may document and/or record your call, which could help you to hold them accountable for misquoting benefits if you have reimbursement problems down the line.

▶ **"But I can never reach a live person!"** For tips on reaching a breathing human being and navigating the automated phone maze, see Page 28.

▶ **Call Jack back and tell him what his portion of the payment for the sessions will be.** Remind him to bring his insurance card to the first session (or have him send via secure email or fax) so you have a copy for your records.

After years of experience, I've come to the conclusion that NOT making this call up front is the biggest error therapists make when working with insurance. Most therapists who consult with me after a claim denial could have avoided lost money and frustrating calls had they called the plan and asked the right questions before treatment. While of course you may tell Jack that he must check his own benefits, and pay whatever portion insurance does not cover, you are the one most likely to be hurt by not making the call.

Checking Benefits

On Page 41, there's a form you can use when you call to check coverage. A few notes:

▶ **"Why are they calling it behavioral health?"** Mental health and substance abuse are known as behavioral health benefits. Just ask for <u>outpatient mental health</u> benefits.

▶ **The insured vs. the client.** No matter who your client will be, you may need to get information about the primary insured, also known as the subscriber or policyholder of the plan, usually the employee in an employer-sponsored plan. The client may be the insured if the policy is his; if the client is using coverage of a spouse, parent, or domestic partner, the spouse, parent, or partner is the insured.

▶ **Having "unlimited sessions" does not always mean unlimited.** Remember that an insurance company may not always authorize a client to use all their benefits. It will depend on many factors, especially whether they think there is a "medical necessity" for the sessions (for more about medical necessity, see Chapter 9).

▶ **Two insurance plans?** Always ask clients if they might be covered by two insurance plans. if so, see Chapter 17 for "double coverage."

▶ **Deductible used up?** When you call the plan, don't forget to ask how much of the client's deductible has been used up for the year. Jack may have a $1500 deductible, but if he (or his family) has already used it up for the year, you don't have to worry – just collect his co-insurance or copayment. If he hasn't used it, the first $1500 of your charges will be out of his pocket. Remember that the deductible is shared with other health in-network providers Jack sees, but he likely has a separate out of network deductible for any out-of-network providers he sees.

▶ **When do benefits renew?** While most plans operate on a calendar year, some operate on a 12-month calendar, starting July 1 or March 1, or other fiscal year time frames. Why does this matter to you? The deductible might start again mid-year, so the plan stops covering sessions while this is used up.

▶ **Don't ask if they cover couples or family therapy.** The plan may say no, when they actually do. They may think you are asking if the client has coverage for sessions focused on relationship issues where no diagnosis exists. Ask instead if CPT code for 90847 and 90846 are covered for a client with a diagnosis. These CPT codes are for a couples or family session from the American Medical Association's Current Procedural Terminology Manual[23] for more on CPT codes see Pages 64-65, Box 24D, and Resources, Page 133; for more on couples/family therapy, see Page 105).

▶ **Usual, Customary and Reasonable fees (UCR).** This applies only to out-of-network providers. UCR is the "allowed amount" the plan feels is reasonable for the service, based on fees for similar providers in your area. Asking about UCRs helps clients predict how much they will be reimbursed. Let's say your fee is $150, which Jack pays at the session, and he has a 50% co-insurance for out-of-network providers. He turns in his invoice from you to CureQuick, and thinks his reimbursement will be $75 (50% of $150). But let's say CureQuick's UCR – the maximum they'll allow for this session – is $100. This means Jack will only be reimbursed $50 (50% of the $100 UCR). Plans won't always tell you their UCR (you may have to wait until the claim is processed). When you call try naming your fee and asking them it is within the UCR. It is recommended you submit the first invoice as soon as possible.

▶ **Out-of-pocket maximum.** The plan may quote an "out-of-pocket maximum." This is the maximum amount Jack must pay before the plan begins to pay 100% of covered expenses. If claims come back paid in full by the plan, the client may have hit this number. Since these maximums are usually high, in most cases this is not essential information, but it may come into play if clients have serious illness or surgery.

▶ **Ask about telehealth coverage.** If you are providing telehealth services, ask all the ask about Jack's telehealth coverage, and his copayment/deductible for this service. Ask if it is paid at the same rate as in-office care, what Place of Service Code and modifier they may require, whether you need to be on their approved telehealth provider list, and any limitations of the coverage.

▶ **Remember: The information you get isn't a guarantee of coverage.** Have clients agree in writing that they are responsible for amounts unpaid by the plan (see treatment agreements, Page 44, and Sample Treatment Agreement, Page 143).

CHECKING COVERAGE: 14 ESSENTIAL QUESTIONS

BEFORE CALLING INSURANCE: INFO TO GET FROM THE CLIENT / CARD

Client: _____ **I.D. # :** _____

Subscriber (if other): _____ **Group:#** _____

Client Birthdate: ____ / ____ / _____ **Releationship to Subscriber:** _____

Subscriber's Employer _____

Insurance Phone Number *(The card may say "MH/SA Benefits," "Eligibility and Benefits," For Pre-Authorization," "Member Service"):* _____

THE CALL: WHAT TO ASK THE INSURANCE COMPANY

CALL DATE: _____ / _____ / _____ **REPRESENTATIVE NAME** _____

Request outpatient mental health benefits." Tell them if you're a network provider.

1. Copayment (flat fee) **or Coinsurance** (percent)	
2. Deductible (if applicable)	
3. Sessions Allowed per Year	
4. When Do Benefits Start & Renew?	**Effective:** ____ / ____ / ____ **Renew:** ____ / ____ / ____
5. Deductible met so far this year	$_____._____
6. Is Pre-authorization Needed? *(for some plans, authorization is needed only after a certain number of sessions)*	No ___ Needed After Visit #___ ▪ If Yes: Auth#: _____ ▪ # of Sessions Authorized:_____ ▪ Start:__ / ___ / ____ Expires:___ / ___ / ____
7. Claim form: HCFA/CMS-1500?	Yes _____ No _____
8. Out-of-pocket Maximum, *amount client pays before plan starts paying 100%*	
9. Claims address for EAP or MENTAL HEALTH claims	
10. Is CPT code 90847(couples / family therapy) **covered?**	Yes _____ No _____
11. Is telehealth covered? *At same rate as in-person? Video and phone? Are client copays/deductibles the same? What modifier/Place of Service code is needed? Is preauthorization needed?*	
12. Am I a network provider for this client's specific plan/account?	
EXTRA: OUT-OF-NETWORK PROVIDERS: **13. Is my license covered?**	Yes _____ No _____
14. Is my fee within the plan's UCR *(Usual, Customary, Reasonable fee)?*	UCR: CPT CODE:_____: $_____ CPT CODE:_____: $_____ CPT CODE:_____: $_____

Translating "Insurance-Speak"

Now for a quiz to see if you can interpret the language of insurance representatives!

For this example, let's say that you have signed a contract with Jack's insurance plan, CureQuick, to see their members at a fee of $67 per session. This is your "contracted rate."

What the Representative Tells You	What Jack Will Have To Pay	What Insurance Will Pay
"He has a $10 copayment, after which he is covered at 100 percent of the contracted rate," or "he is covered at 100 percent with a $10 copayment."	Ignore the "100 percent" part of the sentence. Jack will pay **$10** (his copayment) per session.	**$57.** To calculate, take your contracted rate of $67, and subtract Jack's copayment of $10
"Jack is covered at 70 percent."	Since the plan is paying 70%, Jack must pay 30 percent of your contracted rate of $67, a total of **$20.10** per session.	**$46.90** (70 percent of the contracted rate of $67)
"Jack is covered at 90 percent, up to a maximum of $25 per session."	While you can figure out what 90% of your contracted rate is, the rep is telling you that the most CureQuick will pay per session is $25. Jack pays the difference between the $25 insurance reimbursement and the contracted rate of $67, which is **$42.**	**$25**
"Jack has a deductible of $150, and none of it has been used. After that he is covered at 90 percent.	Here things get interesting. All of Sessions 1 and 2 will go toward the deductible, so Jack will pay $67 for each session, using up $134 of the deductible after Session 2. In Session 3, Jack must pay $16 of your $67 fee to finish the deductible, plus 10 percent of the remaining $51 ($16 + $5.10 = $21.10). After this he will pay 10 percent of your contracted rate, or **$6.70** per session.	For Session 1 and 2, insurance pays $0. For Session 3, the plan pays $45.90 ($67 minus Jack's copay of $21.10). After this, the plan pays 90 percent of $67, or **$60.30** per session.

42

Care Denials: Bad News Before Treatment Begins

When you call to check Jack's coverage, CureQuick may tell you it does not cover the services Jack is seeking. Common reasons might be:

- **Jack is no longer (or not yet) covered by the health plan.** He may have recently left his job or started a new one. There is sometimes a gap between when a client gets a new job and when his insurance "kicks in." Another good reason for checking benefits at the start of treatment!

- **The service you intend to provide is not a covered benefit.** Not all insurance plans, for example, cover group therapy, extended sessions, parenting classes, meditation classes, etc. You may also be refused if it is not clear that a diagnosed mental disorder is being treated.

- **The rep says the plan doesn't cover "couples counseling."** a few plans don't cover couples or family counseling at all. However, most plans will cover couples sessions when the sessions address a diagnosed mental illness in a covered member. To bill for couples therapy, you must feel that one member of the couple has a diagnosis more than a Z-code from the DSM, the Diagnostic and Statistical Manual of the American Psychiatric Association.[24] Typically a relationship problem or phase of life issue alone is not enough). But remember: It is insurance fraud to overstate or create a diagnosis for the purpose of ensuring reimbursement. (For more on couples counseling, see Chapter 17). Ask the plan if CPT code 90847 is covered for the client.

- **Your license is not covered.** Many states have a "Freedom of Choice" law, which states that insurance plans must allow any licensed provider to be considered for the provider panel, and if the client has out of network benefits, that the plan must reimburse when the client sees any licensed out-of-network provider. If your state doesn't have a "Freedom of Choice" law, or the insurance plan was written for delivery in another state, the plan may refuse to cover your license, even if you are in-network with your local plan. I know of one instance where Blue Cross/Blue Shield of Florida did not cover visits to a California Blue Cross <u>in-network</u> Licensed Marriage and Family Therapist, since the MFT license was not covered by their Florida plans. However, don't assume that because the insurance company has an out-of-state address that this will be a problem.

And what if you are denied? Don't be discouraged. Care denials can often be overturned if you know how to approach the relevant issues (see Chapter 13 for a wealth of ideas).

The First Session

In the first session, you might take some time to educate Jack about what it means if he chooses to use his insurance. After reading this manual, hopefully you'll be able to communicate with all your clients about the pros and cons of using insurance, and about confidentiality issues and coverage limitations, so they can make informed choices. Many professional organizations offer a brochure you can give clients on the use of insurance in therapy, or you may want to create your own.

If this is an EAP session, go over Jack's EAP benefit with him. Explain that your role is to assess his situation and determine if it can be resolved within the specified number of sessions or if longer-term counseling and/or a referral is needed. Also let him know about other free assistance that may be available to him via his EAP, such as legal and financial consultations, and referrals for child and elder care.

Reasons for a Treatment Agreement

I highly recommend that you give all new clients a treatment agreement. This agreement (which they will sign) is a form that educates them about how your practice operates, including your fees, the length of sessions, how payment and billing will be handled, the limits of confidentiality, your cancellation policy, termination, and after-hours coverage. It can also be used to inform clients about your insurance policies (see the Sample Treatment Agreement on Page 143). Some sentences that I have seen in providers' agreements to explain their policies include:

▶ *"The client is responsible for verifying and understanding the limits of his/her insurance coverage, as well as for any copayments and deductibles."*

▶ *"The client is responsible for any and all fees not reimbursed by the insurance plan."*

▶ Either *"the therapist is a contracted provider with the client's insurance plan, and has agreed to a specified fee, and will bill the plan on the client's behalf"* or *"the therapist is not a contracted provider with the client's insurance plan. Should the client choose to bill insurance, the therapist will provide the client with a statement of fees paid by the client, which may be submitted by the client to the plan for reimbursement."*

▶ *"The client must pay all insurance copayments and deductibles, if applicable, at the time of the session."*

▶ *"If the client misses a session or cancels without 24-hour notice, he/she is responsible for paying the therapist's missed session fee of $_____ (not just the insurance copayment). Insurance plans typically will not reimburse for missed sessions."*

▶ *"By signing this form, the client authorizes the release of any information including diagnosis, prognosis, and treatment information needed to process insurance or EAP claims, for billing purposes, to gain approval for additional sessions, to verify medical necessity of the sessions, or to satisfy the insurance plan's administrative audits or quality reviews."*

▶ *"By signing below, the client authorizes insurance payments to be made to the therapist"* (omit this if clients will pay you in full and bill insurance themselves).

▶ *"By signing below, you acknowledge receipt of the Notice of Privacy Practices, as required by HIPAA"* (Note: Include this if you are a HIPAA "covered entity" – more on this in Chapter 7).

The Insurance Card – And Why You Shouldn't Trust It

PAILS "R" US

CureQuick
Behavioral Health   Wonderland HMO
www.curequick.com

GROUP: 23560   Deductible: $1500
                     Office copayment: $10

MEMBER ID: PRU34567   Specialist: $25

JACK ISA KLUTZ

Plan 040: Wellquick Pharmacy – Medical

This card does not prove membership nor guarantee
coverage. For verification of benefits, please call
Customer Service.

Providers: For self-service, go to www.curequick.com
Or call Customer Service: 1-800-555-3975

Claims: 12 HARVEY DRIVE, SUMMIT, N.J. 07901

Customer Service: 1-800-555-5554
For MH/SA benefits, call 1-800-555-5555
Pharmacy: 1-800-555-5544

In session one, copy both sides of Jack's card, and keep a copy in his chart. Look for the phone number to call for mental health benefits. It might say "for Eligibility and Benefits" or simply "Customer Service." In Jack's case, you will see the back of his card has two phone numbers. The one you want is labeled "for MH/SA," which means "for mental health and substance abuse benefits."

So why not trust insurance cards?

► **The copay and deductible info may not apply to mental health,** it may apply to medical services. Or with a PPO it may say he has a $1000 deductible, but you might find he already used it, or it is waived if he uses a network provider. And it gives two possible two copay amounts – are you a specialist? You'll need to check.

► **The claims address may not apply to you.** Often, the claims address is for medical claims, not mental health, and the mental health claims address is not even printed on the card. Do not assume the claims address is the same as CureQuick's corporate address, or the address where you mail other information.

► **Even the name of the insurance company on the card might be irrelevant.** Often mental health services have been "carved out." This means CureQuick may have hired another company to manage mental health benefits. Why is this important to you? Jack may call and tell you he has benefits with CureQuick (for which you are a network provider), but later you find out his mental health benefits are handled by another plan, in which you are not a network provider. This is another reason to call the insurance plan before the client comes for the first session. Of course, this can work the other way: clients who tell you they have one plan (of which you are not a provider) may turn out to have mental health provided by another plan, where you are a provider, so you will be covered -- but you will have to refund money to the clients since you charged my normal fee for those sessions.

The Perils of Private Pay: When a Client Doesn't Tell You About Coverage

After paying full fee out-of-pocket for three months, Jack surprises you by mentioning that he has CureQuick insurance, and asks you to bill the plan for past sessions. You are a CureQuick provider. Are you obligated to refund Jack for all monies paid for those three months, minus copayments and his deductible?

When a new client begins therapy and doesn't mention insurance, you may understandably assume he isn't covered. But he may be so distressed he forgets to mention it. He may have planned to come only for a few sessions, but as treatment costs mount he may look for ways to finance therapy. Or he may not have realized that his insurance covers therapy.

Is it really our responsibility to find out if clients have insurance? Well, like it or not, the bottom line is that it can blow up in your face If you don't ask up front, as in this scenario. If you are a plan provider, you agreed in your contract to charge all plan members only their copayment and any deductibles, and to bill the plan directly on the client's behalf. The only time you are relieved of this obligation is when a client has specifically asked you <u>not</u> to bill his insurance. From the standpoint of the insurance company, if a client asks to use his insurance, contracted providers need to accept it.

So, what do you do now? Bill the plan for the sessions, and hopefully you will be paid. Then figure out what the client should have paid according to his coverage, and refund the client the difference. If your claims are denied due to "lack of authorization" or "late filing," file an appeal, explaining the situation, and ask the plan to reconsider their denial. Another option: as an acknowledgement that your client did not inform you of their coverage, and that it might be too late for you to get paid for sessions, you might ask your client if he would be willing to just have you bill insurance going forward (if so, get this in writing).

So, what is the lesson? In the first session, ask ALL clients – even private-pay clients – if they have ANY medical insurance. If they have some insurance but you don't think you are covered, call and check – as I said earlier, network affiliations can be complicated, so you may be a plan provider when you don't think you are. Have all clients whose treatment is not covered by insurance (or who are choosing not to use it) sign a Private Pay Agreement, where the client attests that he does not have insurance coverage, or has insurance coverage but chooses not to use it, waiving reimbursement rights (a sample Private Pay Agreement is on Page 149).

9

Treatment Reviews, Medical Necessity, and Progress Notes

ℰℴ ℭ℘

So, you've been working with Jack, and naturally he is improving under your expert care. However, while he is doing better, he continues to have intrusive anxiety and sleep problems. You get a call from the insurance plan asking to review treatment.

Treatment Reviews and Medical Necessity

Insurance companies may periodically review treatment in order to monitor the effectiveness of the care you are providing, and the clinical need ("medical necessity") for continued care. While parity laws have done away with most plans' yearly session limits, plans retain the right to review treatment and to limit it based on medical necessity criteria.

It's important to remember that while treatment reviews are usually conducted on the care of network providers, they can also be required from out-of-network providers. As soon as an invoice or claim is submitted for treatment, the door is opened for a treatment review. They are more frequently requested for HMO clients than for PPO clients.

The treatment reviews may be by phone, or you may need to fill out a request form provided by the plan, sometimes called the Outpatient Treatment Report (OTR) or Request for Reauthorization (RFR). This form can often be filled out online at the company's website, or downloaded and faxed to the insurance plan. If approved, you will usually receive an authorization in the mail or by fax.

What will they ask? Using a checklist and/or a narrative format, the plan may ask the client's diagnosis, symptoms and symptom severity, level of impairment, progress made, why you feel there is a need for ongoing treatment, treatment goals, and planned interventions for the next phase of therapy.

How often do I have to request more sessions, and what could trigger a review?

You may find most of your clients have unlimited sessions, so you shouldn't have to ask for more sessions all year. But this doesn't mean your treatment might not be reviewed. Susan Frager, a former case manager, writes that in some plans "case managers focus their efforts only on cases where the patient is not progressing, where utilization [number of visits used] is higher than average, or on patients with chronic, severe conditions that need careful management to avoid multiple hospitalizations."[25.] Meeting with a client more than once a week for several months or for regular extended sessions might trigger a review. However, some health plans ask for a Treatment Update to be completed after a certain number of sessions, and scrutinize care to see if the symptoms warrant treatment, or if therapy is simply desired by the client for personal growth.

What Case Managers Look For: "Medical Necessity"

Health insurance contracts are written for the purpose of covering sickness and illness. Therefore, the insurance company staff member who is reviewing your authorization request will be looking for the medical need for treatment. This means that he or she must be convinced that a psychiatric condition or illness is being treated, and that the treatment is necessary and appropriate to treat the symptoms or illness.

What does this really mean? While medical necessity criteria vary between insurance plans, here are some common components that can give us a clue about what the folks at CureQuick might be looking for when they look over your request for sessions:

▶ **Medical symptoms and a diagnosis.** Jack must show symptoms consistent with a diagnosis from the American Medical Association's most *International Statistical Classification of Diseases (ICD)* or the American Psychiatric Association's *Diagnostic and Statistical Manual of Mental Disorders (DSM)*.[26, 27] The two manuals share virtually the same coding for psychiatric disorders, so when you are using the DSM codes, you are using the ICD codes (more about this on Page 64, Box 21). The client usually needs a primary diagnosis that is more than uncomplicated grief or a phase of life problem (what were called V-codes in the past, then Z-Codes in the DSM-5). And avoid "Unspecified" diagnoses and common sexual disorders -- many plans don't cover these. This goes to show that just because a client has a diagnosis in the book doesn't mean that makes their treatment medically necessary in the eyes of the insurance plan.

▶ **Treatment must focus on reduction of these medical symptoms** (such as anxiety, depression, and insomnia). The sole or primary focus of treatment cannot simply be personal growth, self-esteem, financial problems, career issues, inadequate communication skills, an annoying spouse or in-law, or parenting issues.

▶ **A decrease in functioning.** The symptoms are significant enough to have led to a decrease in functioning in at least one area as compared to Jack's pre-illness or baseline level of functioning (be able to articulate how).

▶ **Therapy is deemed appropriate** and within accepted standards of care for the symptoms, diagnosis, or treatment of Jack's condition. It is believed to be the most

48

appropriate type and length of treatment, and it isn't primarily for Jack's convenience (or yours).

▶ **There is an expectation that Jack has the capacity to make progress toward treatment goals** or that treatment is necessary to maintain the current level of functioning. At the very least, the plan must feel you are stabilizing the client enough to prevent hospitalization.

▶ **The client is engaged in treatment.** Jack must be motivated and participating in treatment, attending sessions and following recommendations.

▶ **The problem seems resolvable, and the treatment is working.** If CureQuick feels that it has paid for too much therapy without improvement, they may conclude Jack's problem cannot be resolved in outpatient therapy, or may need some alternative type or level of care. Clients who are not insight-oriented or have reached therapeutic plateaus may be considered more appropriate for referral to community support groups for maintenance.

▶ **The client is receiving the proper level of treatment given his level of functioning.** If you report a very low level of functioning, the reviewer may feel the client may belong in a higher level or intensity of treatment. If you report a high level of functioning, the plan may feel the client's treatment is no longer medically necessary, and that he could be referred to a community support, such as a self-help group.

▶ **They often want a treatment plan in place**, documented separately in your chart or at least evident in your session notes, which you have discussed with the client. Is it clear to you and the client what you are working on, how it will be worked on, how you will know when it is time to end treatment, and what supports will be in place at that point to prevent relapse?

▶ **When appropriate, clients have been referred for a medication evaluation.**

▶ **You've documented coordination of care** with doctors and other treating providers.

▶ **When working with a child or adolescent,** your treatment plan typically must include some family therapy, unless contraindicated.

▶ **It is believed the client could not achieve the same functioning level with medication and community resources alone.**

In addition, those evaluating your requests will check for potential risk issues, such as suicidal and homicidal ideation, chemical dependency, domestic violence, or abuse issues.

A Sample Narrative Treatment Update

Reading treatment reviews is time-consuming and costly to the insurance company. Therefore, the trend seems to be away from asking for a narrative summary of treatment. But in case you are asked to write a narrative summary with interventions and goals, here is an example that might give you some pointers:

Current Symptoms: Client continues to report moderate depression and anxiety, including weekly nightmares of the fall and daytime flashbacks of moderate intensity that occur twice weekly. Depressive symptoms include loss of pleasure, loss of appetite, loss of weight (12 lbs. in 4 weeks), and insomnia. Client continues to experience phobic response when near pails, including heart racing, dizziness, waves of panic, a desire to flee, and nausea. Because his job involves frequent exposure to pails, he remains on restricted duty, which has put a financial strain on family. He is irritable, and has withdrawn from social interaction. Says family relationships have been negatively affected due to his irritability and depression.

Client Progress Summary: Client reports less flashbacks and nightmares, and lower overall anxiety since starting therapy. Insomnia has decreased from daily to twice weekly. Using sleep tools learned in therapy, now reports 7 hours sleep nightly (up from 5 hours), but still reports difficulty falling asleep. Scores on both the Burns Anxiety and Depression Inventories have decreased since start of therapy but are still in Moderate Range.

Interventions: To reduce anxiety: Use systematic desensitization to help client manage anxiety while he visualizes being near pails again. Teach anxiety coping skills, including relaxation, meditation, and visualization. Using Cognitive Behavioral Therapy, teach client to identify distorted cognitions that increase anxiety and depression, using journaling, and written exercises from Anxiety Workbook. Recommend physical exercise, and assist client in increasing social support system. Refer to Mindfulness-Based Stress Relaxation class. Give insomnia audiotapes to listen to nightly. Refer for medication evaluation if symptoms persist and monitor adherence to medication regime.

Goals: Client will be able to return to work, and be able to be near a pail with no more than mild anxiety. Client will report less insomnia, and nightmares and flashbacks not more than twice monthly each, of milder severity and duration, which do not interfere with functioning. Periods of intense anxiety will be less frequent and of shorter duration. Client will demonstrate lower scores on the Burns Anxiety and Depression Inventories – in Mild Range. Weight loss will stop, and appetite will return. Client will take any medications as prescribed, report practicing relaxation and coping techniques at least once daily, and use support system as needed to help him cope.

Treatment Review: Dos and Don'ts

Do:

▶ **Focus on symptoms, and be specific.** Remember, this is the medical model, so communicate in this language. List the symptoms the client is experiencing that have led to a decrease in his or her usual level of functioning. Replace casual language such as "stressed" with more clinical language such as "anxious." List specific clinical symptoms, severity and frequency, and scores on diagnostic tests. Include how the diagnosis has affected his "activities of daily living" (ADLs) such as work, family, friendships, finances, self-care, etc. Focus on current symptoms that support the diagnosis, and avoid irrelevant details.

▶ **Address how treatment will reduce impairment.** How will it reduce symptoms? And how do the sessions avoid the need for more intensive/expensive care? Remember, cost containment is one of the goals of an insurance company, so keep this in mind when conversing with case managers.

▶ **If asked about your goals,** make sure they are clear, measurable, realistic, and consistent with the presenting problem and diagnosis.   Identify how you will know if the desired change has taken place. As in the narrative example above, try to quantify treatment goals. Don't focus goals on personal growth.

▶ **Explain your interventions** (what you plan to do in session or through homework to help the client achieve the goals). Again, see the example on the previous page. Avoid sentences such as "help Jack identify feelings about coworkers," "provide support," "validate," or "build rapport." Those are expected from any therapist. What will you do or teach the client to reduce symptoms?

▶ **Try to identify any areas of progress you see, however small.** Less days of work missed? Less suicidal ideation? But don't worry -- case managers understand that progress isn't always linear and smooth, and that your client may even have setbacks in treatment.

▶ **Document any referrals for medication evaluation.** With clients who have a major mood disorder, a referral for medications should be discussed with the client. Document this discussion, and referrals made, even if the client refuses to follow-up.

▶ **Document your referrals to community resources.** This includes referrals to 12-Step programs, treatment facilities, classes or support groups, even if refused.

▶ **Document a safety plan** when the client is a danger to self or others or gravely disabled.

Don'ts

▶ **Don't be vague.** A common complaint of case managers is that our treatment plans lack specific goals or progress criteria. Vague treatment goals may lead to denials, or lead the care manager to authorize limited sessions and a follow-up interview.

▶ **Don't try to solve all the client's problems.** Identify goals that can realistically be achieved within a few months, if possible.

▶ **You don't have to aim for symptom elimination.** Remember that insurance companies may not feel they need to continue to cover a client until the symptoms have vanished. In some cases, returning the client to baseline functioning -- or stabilizing at an acceptable level of functioning and referring to community support -- may be all they will cover.

▶ **Avoid too much theoretical speculation.** Don't focus on enmeshment, differentiation, attachment difficulties, projecting, or any theoretical buzzwords. Don't talk about the inner child or unconscious introjects. Think medical and observable symptoms, like anxiety, depression, or insomnia.

▶ **Don't dwell on the past.** Don't bring up the client's past, unless it is directly relevant and directly impacts the client's present impairment. Even then, keep it brief. Stay focused on current symptoms.

▶ **Don't just list stressors.** Saying your client needs more sessions since he just filed for divorce does not give the case manager enough information to understand the symptoms that this particular client is experiencing.

▶ **Don't list poor self-esteem as a sole treatment focus.** Saying that a client has come to treatment to deal with low self-esteem can be the kiss of death. Insurance companies don't see improving low self-esteem alone as "medically necessary."

▶ **Don't be afraid to say if the client is doing worse.** However, explain this, if possible, and identify any new problems that have come up since treatment began. Alter your treatment plan to reflect the new situation.

▶ **Don't reveal any more information than you must.** In cases where you feel you need to disclose sensitive information in order to get more sessions, you might discuss this with the client (and document the conversation) so he can make an informed choice about whether to release that information. Jack may decide he would rather pay out of pocket than reveal this information.

▶ **Don't just repeat or copy your last authorization request**, even if little has changed. The lack of new information may trigger a case manager's review.

How About When Things Get Better?

It sometimes happens that your client no longer meets the criteria for medical necessity, yet you still feel the client needs ongoing care to address underlying or chronic issues. You may be concerned that these issues, if left untreated, could result in a regression of the client's symptoms. A client with a history of recurrent depression, a background of childhood abuse, or with perpetual problems with intimacy in relationships could fall into this category. If your client no longer meets the criteria for medical necessity, you have several choices: You can argue (and document) the need for maintenance sessions to prevent relapse, request more sessions to do wrap-up and discharge planning, or stop billing insurance and contract with the client to pay out of pocket (be sure to have them sign a Private Pay Agreement; see Sample Private Pay Agreement, Page 159).

Why Your Request Might Get a Closer Look

Let's look at why your request for more sessions might get a closer examination or outright denial:

▶ **It's incomplete, illegible, or too vague.**

▶ **It is a copy of what you wrote last time.**

▶ **Great progress.** If Jack's symptoms are mild and your report of his progress is too impressive, the insurance company may conclude that treatment is no longer medically necessary, and Jack is well enough to leave your care. This may be one of the most common reason why further sessions may not be approved.

▶ **No progress.** You've worked with Jack for some time with no improvement. The insurance company may consider discontinuing, or conclude that a different level or type of treatment is necessary.

► **You are ignoring a potential substance abuse issue.** Perhaps they don't feel you have adequately assessed for this, or if you have diagnosed a drug or alcohol problem, you didn't discuss in your treatment plan a referral to a 12-step program or to treatment program for evaluation.

► **There is no medication evaluation.** This might happen if you have diagnosed Jack as having Major Depression or Bipolar Disorder, but he is not on medications, and you have not referred him for a medication evaluation or explained why you did not make such a referral.

► **You deferred the diagnosis.** You need to give a working diagnosis. You can always change it later as your assessment continues, if needed.

► **If you're asking to see Jack several times a week, if you've used a lot of sessions, or if Jack seems highly impaired, the case manager may question why Jack is not in a higher level of care.** Don't be defensive. "Questions from the case manager regarding whether a client needs more intensive treatment are generally not a reflection of the case manager's opinion of the therapist's abilities," former case manager Susan Frager explains.[28] "Part of the case manager's job...is to consider whether another level of care would be more effective at helping the client reach the same treatment goals while conserving limited benefits."

► **Personality disorder.** With some personality disorder diagnoses, your case could undergo closer review. Treatment goals will need to be especially realistic, and coordination of care might be especially important.

► **You have a single case agreement with the plan, or your clients have complained.** In these situations, your treatment reports may get additional scrutiny. See page 25 for more on Single Case Agreements.

Questions and Answers

What if Jack wants to use his insurance, but in our initial session it becomes clear to me that he does not meet the criteria for medical necessity?

Good question. You could explain to Jack that while he may be able to benefit from therapy, from what he has said thus far you do not have evidence that he has a mental illness that would be covered by his health insurance. You might also explain that it would be insurance fraud if you were to make up a diagnosis just so that he is covered, and that doing so could place your license in jeopardy. You might frame this as good news for him, as he will not have a diagnosis in his medical records that could cause problems for him down the line. You may want to call the health plan to check if they will cover this initial assessment session where no diagnosis criteria are met. You can tell him you would be happy to work with him on his presenting problems, but be clear that he would need to pay out of his pocket, and have him sign a Private Pay Agreement (see Sample Private-Pay Agreement on Page 159). Another option would be to use a provisional diagnosis for a few sessions while you do a more thorough assessment, seeing if some diagnosis is indeed appropriate.

What Should Be in Your Client Notes—But Probably Isn't

While I could devote a whole book to progress notes and treatment plans, here is a quick overview.

Detailed notes have always been your best defense in case of a client complaint to a licensing board or ethics committee. Yet many of us still take notes as if we are the only ones who will ever see them.

In addition, insurance plans are reviewing provider charts more than in the past, for a host of administrative reasons. More importantly, your notes may be necessary to back up a client's need for treatment. Your vague or absent notes could actually mean your client might not get treatment approval for necessary sessions.

After serving on the Ethics Committee for a state therapist professional association, I saw how often in a complaint it came down to the client's version of events versus the therapist's word – since the therapist did not have good notes (or any notes) to back up what transpired.

In almost any health plan's provider manual, you will find a list of requirements for what must be in your charts and progress notes. For example, Anthem writes "taking guidance from the Centers for Medicare & Medicaid Services (CMS), Anthem requires that medical record documentation should be legible, signed (including licensure and/or certification), dated, and must contain, at a minimum, the following elements in addition to any state required components:

1. The patient's name documented on each page of the record
2. The date of service documented on each page of the record
3. Type of service (diagnostic assessment, individual, family, group psychotherapy)
4. Start and end times
5. Problem statement (including diagnosis)
6. Support for 54
7. Service rendered including therapeutic interventions
8. Person-centered detail such as behavior description or quotes
9. Patient observation
10. Progress toward goals (lack of progress should result in change in treatment plan)"[29]

Documentation for intake sessions may also need to include symptoms; problem and problem history; psychiatric history including hospitalizations; medications (including over-the-counter), prescribing doctor and contact info; psychosocial information; medical issues and history, and allergies; assessment of risk factors (danger self or others); substance abuse assessment (alcohol/drug/cigarette); support systems; emergency contact info; diagnosis; and medical necessity for treatment and functional impairment(s).

Details about symptom frequency, severity, duration, and examples to establish the need for treatment are as important as details about your in-session interventions and homework.

All this is even a good idea for out-of-network providers, since whenever a client requests reimbursement from a plan, your records may be requested by that plan. You may also need them to defend yourself from a licensing board complaint, or they may be requested in a lawsuit or client disability case. (Do your notes cover all the above requirements? Does the idea of an insurance plan looking at your charts send a chill up your spine? Would you like to see sample progress notes? Check out my webinar *What Should Be In Your Client Charts: Writing Great Progress Notes and Treatment Plans* – See Resources, Page 133)

10

Ongoing Therapy

ಐ ೞ

So, Jack has been coming to see you, and naturally, is progressing amazingly under your excellent treatment.

Feel free to pat yourself on the back! But here are a few things to keep in mind as you continue to work with him:

- ▶ **Be aware of your client's benefits.** While most plans now allow unlimited sessions, a few plans still limit the number of sessions per year. This may make a difference in how you space sessions. If you have limited sessions, keep track of the number of authorized sessions remaining, and the expiration date.

- ▶ **Deductible details.** As was explained in Chapter 2, if you are a network provider and Jack has a deductible, you must collect your contracted rate (not your full fee for private-pay clients) for each session until the deductible is satisfied. You still need to submit the bill to Jack's insurance (or, if you are an out-of-network provider, have Jack submit it) so that his payments will be counted toward his deductible; otherwise, the insurance plan will not be aware that he has met his deductible.

- ▶ **New Year?** If Jack has a deductible, you'll typically need to collect it in the first sessions of the New Year. But don't assume you know how much it is. <u>When Jack's benefits renew, usually in January, call his insurance plan!</u> It's a hassle, but it's worth it to avoid later problems. Jack may have a new plan, or his plan may have a new benefit structure. Here's an all-too-common scenario: Jack is unaware his deductible has gone up from $500 to $1000, and his copayment increased from $10 to $25. By the time your January claims are processed and returned to you without a check, Jack may owe you hundreds of dollars. He may have discontinued therapy, making it harder to collect.

- ▶ **Document changes in diagnosis.** As treatment progresses you might reconsider your initial diagnosis, or the client's symptoms may change. Be sure to document your new or additional diagnosis (and the symptoms that led to it) in the client's chart, and change it on future claim forms.

▶ **Job changes may mean coverage changes.** If Jack leaves his job, be sure to check for insurance coverage loss or changes (see section below on "Losing Coverage").

▶ **Insurance authorizations are sometimes flexible.** As was suggested in the previous chapter, you can sometimes get case managers to extend the expiration date on an authorization if your client hasn't used all his allotted sessions. For example, if Jack has been given twelve sessions to see you, and has only used ten of those by the authorization's expiration date, it may only involve a simple phone call to get the insurance company to extend the expiration date.

▶ **Don't keep the doctor away.** Insurance plans want you to keep the client's physician, psychiatrist, and all other treating health professionals in the loop. Get a release from your client. If Jack refuses, document the refusal and reason in your notes. Care coordination is especially important if the client has a significant health issue, has substance abuse issues (or a history of addiction), or is taking psychiatric medications. Additional contact is recommended when the client is not progressing, unstable, at risk, or when there are significant changes in the client's condition.

▶ **If you need to refer Jack to another provider,** such as a doctor, a psychiatrist, a psychiatric hospital program or substance abuse treatment program, contact the insurance company (or look at the provider directory on the plan's website) for referrals within his plan. Remember that the client may need pre-authorization for this care, especially for inpatient or structured outpatient programs.

▶ **Insurance plans (and some state laws, licensing boards, and ethics codes) expect you to create a treatment plan for every client at the beginning of treatment.** Treatment plans should include your treatment goals, objectives (how you will measure these goals have been achieved), your intended treatment modality and interventions, and dates you feel each goal can reasonably be achieved. Goals and objectives should be specific, measurable, realistic, and focused on symptom-reduction. As you go through treatment, you can add new goals that come up along the way. It is a good idea to review the treatment plan periodically throughout treatment with the client, noting progress, and checking off goals, as appropriate. (For more on Progress Notes, see Page 54. For more on Treatment Plans, see my webinar on Progress Notes and Treatment Plans -- see Resources, Page 133).

Losing Coverage

When a client goes through a major life change like divorce or the loss of a job, the possibility of losing health insurance coverage may be the last thing on his mind. But it should be on yours, as it could impact therapy.

If your client loses his employer-sponsored group coverage, in certain situations -- such as when a company changes health plans -- the new insurance plan may pay for you to have a certain number of transitional sessions with the client, to allow the client time to terminate or to transition to a provider in his new network (for more about Single Case Agreements or Transition of Care Agreements, see Page 25). You might consider using this time to apply to become a provider in the client's new health plan, or to explain to the client the option of contacting his new or former plan to initiate a Single Case Agreement (for more about SCAs, see Page 25).

The client, of course, may choose to continue to see you, paying out of pocket. In this case, have him sign a Private-Pay Agreement (such as the Sample Private Pay Agreement on Page 149), documenting that he understands there has been a change in the payment agreement.

You might also ask your client if he is eligible for COBRA coverage. COBRA (Consolidated Omnibus Budget Reconciliation Act) is a federal statute that requires employers to offer employees and dependents who would otherwise lose their insurance the opportunity to purchase the same coverage the employer provides to its employees. COBRA is available for clients who lost coverage when they were fired, quit their jobs, had work hours cut to a level that they lost their eligibility for coverage, became disabled, divorced, lost their dependent child status, or when the employee died. If Jack lost his job at Pails "R" Us, and was in danger of losing his CureQuick coverage, he could apply for COBRA. This would entitle him to continue with the same coverage he had while employed, but he would take over payment of the premium (the monthly or yearly cost paid to receive the insurance coverage). No physical exam is required. But he must act fast to sign up so there is no break in coverage (breaks can jeopardize the ability to get later coverage). There are also limits to this continuation of coverage (usually 18 months for loss of employment or work hour reduction, 29 months for disability-related events, or 36 months for dependents who would lose coverage for reasons other than employment loss by the employee).[30]

If your client switches to COBRA coverage, what does this mean for you? If the client submitted his COBRA application in a timely fashion and it was processed smoothly, nothing should change in your billing. You keep submitting claims, and the plan continues to pay, as if the client was still employed, since all that has changed is who is paying the premium. But there may be a gap between when the client's coverage terminated and the COBRA coverage begins; the client's claims may be denied until the coverage restarts, at which time coverage is usually backdated to cover the gap. You may have to call the plan to have the claims reprocessed.

If your client has exhausted COBRA benefits, he may then be eligible for individual (non-employer based) coverage through any health plan or a plan offered by his state health exchange through www.healthcare.gov. For details about these plans and other health plans for clients in this position contact your state's Department of Insurance or Department of Managed Care (see Appendix A, Page 129).

Questions and Answers

How often will a case manager call to discuss a case?

Again, this depends on the insurance company, how much work you do with insurance, whether your treatment tends to be brief, and the difficulty of the cases you happen to have. You may never be called. Even though about 95% of my full-time practice is insurance clients, I am called by a case manager only about once a year. One insurance company representative told me that while her company had done away with the authorization request process, they still contact providers occasionally to check on progress in cases where you are regularly doing multiple sessions per week, or routinely doing extended sessions, or the amount of sessions had significantly exceeded what would be expected for the diagnosis. Of course, keep in mind sometimes you will be called as part of random selection of cases to review.

Will the plan cover Eye Movement Desensitization Reprocessing (EMDR)?

I am happy to say that insurance plans typically will cover EMDR, seeing it as a proven treatment when medically necessary and when provided by a qualified behavioral health provider. Some plan will only feel it is appropriate to be used to treat clients who meet the diagnosis of Post-Traumatic Stress Disorder, or possibly Acute Stress Disorder or other Anxiety Disorders. However, plans may not cover it for other diagnoses, considering it unproven. The biggest issue may come if you do extended sessions -- longer than 60 minutes -- and want to be reimbursed by the plan (see Extended Sessions, Page 68). If you run into difficulties with approvals or reimbursement, try submitting research related to EMDR's effectiveness with your client's diagnosis. One client I knew could not find an EMDR therapist on her health plan, and convinced her plan to negotiate a Single Case Agreement with an EMDR-trained therapist who was not on her network. The therapist was able to get her full fee for the sessions (see Single Case Agreements, Page 25).

What happens if a client complains about me to the health plan?

You should always take the pro-active approach and call the plan if you suspect a member is unhappy with you, before they call the plan. Take care to document these cases carefully in case a complaint is later filed. If the member makes a complaint, you will be contacted for a response, a request will likely be made for copies of your records and other supporting documentation, and the situation will typically be reviewed by other clinicians at the health plan. What happens next will depends on the severity and type of accusation. But the emphasis is usually on improving quality of care and member service, not punishment, so most insurance plans will work with providers toward this end, whenever possible.

Will insurance cover my time when responding to a client who calls in emergency?

Usually not. Historically, insurance plans have not covered phone-only treatment of any kind. If you contact the plan and telephone sessions are covered, it will need to be at least 16 minutes to bill as a 90832. If not covered, you could schedule a video or face-to-face session as soon as possible, if these are covered. You shouldn't charge the client for an emergency call unless telephone emergency intervention fees were agreed on in writing at the start of treatment. Most plans cover emergency room services. In fact, some states have laws that forbid plans from denying payment for emergency services at any hospital -- even if the situation is later discovered not to be an emergency -- if any prudent layperson would have considered it to be an emergency. Plans expect you to have some sort of emergency coverage, such as an answering service. In addition, in your outgoing voicemail message, clients should be directed to call 911 or go to the emergency room in case you are unable to be reached in an emergency.

11

Getting Paid
Submitting Claims and Giving Invoices
∞ ∞

You've been working with Jack for a month, and you decide to submit claims to CureQuick.

Now, I know you are in this line of work because you care so much about humankind, but let's face it -- we've all got expenses to pay, so understanding the insurance billing and payment process is important. This is essential even if you never join a provider network, as in all likelihood you will be providing some type of invoice to some clients to submit to their insurance plan. So, let's review the billing differences:

If You are a Network Provider:

▶ You should put your full fee on the claim form, not your contracted rate. An adjustment will be made by CureQuick before you are paid.

▶ You must take care of billing CureQuick on Jack's behalf. At the session, Jack pays only the copayment or co-insurance, and any deductible, if applicable.

▶ In your contract, you agreed to accept CureQuick's rate as payment in full for your services. You can't "balance-bill" Jack for the difference between your usual fee and the discounted amount CureQuick pays you.

If You are an Out-of-Network Provider:

▶ If you HAVEN'T signed a contract with the plan, Jack is a private pay client. This means you can charge your full fee, or you may choose to offer a discounted or "sliding scale" fee.

▶ If Jack wants to seek insurance reimbursement, you may give him an invoice/Superbill to submit to his insurance plan (see Sample Invoice, Page 145). A CMS-1500 form can also be used as an invoice for the plan, but sometimes this confuses the plan into thinking you are a plan provider.

Does being an out-of-network provider sound good now? Of course. But remember, only network providers receive referrals from the plan, and Jack would not have come to you without this referral.

The CMS-1500 Claim Form (formerly the HCFA-1500)

While a few insurance plans and many EAPs require their own claim form, the CMS-1500 is the standard claim form accepted by most plans. Distributed by the Center for Medicare and Medicaid Services (CMS), this form is often still called the HCFA-1500, its former name when the CMS was the Health Care Financing Administration. This form is generally used by network providers, and can be used by solo practitioners, groups, and facilities billing for outpatient services (if you are a facility billing for inpatient services or an intensive outpatient program, you may need to use a UB-92 form instead).

A sample of the CMS-1500 appears on the next page. Following that is a chart that gives line-by-line instructions and tips for filling out the form. A few notes:

▶ **Be sure you have the latest version of this form.** The latest version as of this printing is version 02/12, and is to be used for all dates of service. Plans may deny a claim filed on an older version. You can tell you have the latest version if you see a black square "QR" code in the upper left-hand corner of the form. If scanned by a smartphone's barcode reader or other barcode scanner, this code will take users to the website for the National Uniform Claim Commission (NUCC), where they can get more information about the form (for ideas where to buy the forms, see Resources, Page 133).

▶ **Can you handwrite these forms or make a copy of a blank form and use this as a template?** It isn't recommended. For fastest processing, if not electronically submitting claims, health plans may recommend or require that your claims should be:
    1. Submitted on the original red CMS-1500 forms (Medicare does not accept photocopies, and private plans may soon follow suit)
    2. Typed or computer-printed, using black ink, with block capital letters (private health plans have started to reject handwritten claims)
    3. Free of crossed-out or typed-over mistakes (some plans suggest you use only lift-off correction tape to make corrections), and
    4. Neatly filled out, so that data does not overlap into other blocks.

    Why? Most plans use computer scanners that can only read typed characters on the original red forms. If it can be read by a computer, it can go to a paid status, sometimes as quickly as within 24 hours of receipt. However, photocopied or handwritten claims will require hand-processing, which can significantly delay your payment and increase the chance of denial. In fact, United Behavioral Health once reported that "UBH receives more than 2,000 illegible handwritten claims a day."[31] Thus if you don't submit electronically, it may be worth purchasing the original red forms and a software program that allows you to print claims -- there are many inexpensive billing programs available (for tips on where to get claims or billing programs, see Resources, Page 133).

▶ **Submit via mail, fax, or electronically?** Find out which the plan accepts – then it is up to you, but electronic billing typically leads to fastest payment (see Chapter 14 for more on electronic billing).

HEALTH INSURANCE CLAIM FORM

APPROVED BY NATIONAL UNIFORM CLAIM COMMITTEE (NUCC) 02/12

| | PICA | | | | | | | PICA | |

| 1. MEDICARE (Medicare#) | MEDICAID (Medicaid#) | TRICARE (ID#/DoD#) | CHAMPVA (Member ID#) | GROUP HEALTH PLAN (ID#) [X] | FECA BLK LUNG (ID#) | OTHER (ID#) | 1a. INSURED'S I.D. NUMBER (For Program in Item 1) XDM12345678 |

2. PATIENT'S NAME (Last Name, First Name, Middle Initial)
KLUTZ, JACK, A

3. PATIENT'S BIRTH DATE MM 02 DD 01 YY 1961 **SEX** M [X] F [ ]

4. INSURED'S NAME (Last Name, First Name, Middle Initial)
KLUTZ, JACK, A

5. PATIENT'S ADDRESS (No., Street)
123 WATER STREET

6. PATIENT RELATIONSHIP TO INSURED
Self [X] Spouse [ ] Child [ ] Other [ ]

7. INSURED'S ADDRESS (No., Street)
123 WATER STREET

CITY HILLTOWN STATE CA

8. RESERVED FOR NUCC USE

CITY HILLTOWN STATE CA

ZIP CODE 95123 TELEPHONE (Include Area Code) (408) 5551234

ZIP CODE 95123 TELEPHONE (Include Area Code) (408) 5551234

9. OTHER INSURED'S NAME (Last Name, First Name, Middle Initial)

10. IS PATIENT'S CONDITION RELATED TO:

11. INSURED'S POLICY GROUP OR FECA NUMBER
55123

a. OTHER INSURED'S POLICY OR GROUP NUMBER

a. EMPLOYMENT? (Current or Previous) YES [ ] NO [X]

a. INSURED'S DATE OF BIRTH MM 02 DD 01 YY 1961 **SEX** M [X] F [ ]

b. RESERVED FOR NUCC USE

b. AUTO ACCIDENT? YES [ ] NO [X] PLACE (State)

b. OTHER CLAIM ID (Designated by NUCC)

c. RESERVED FOR NUCC USE

c. OTHER ACCIDENT? YES [ ] NO [X]

c. INSURANCE PLAN NAME OR PROGRAM NAME
SECURE CHOICE PPO

d. INSURANCE PLAN NAME OR PROGRAM NAME

10d. CLAIM CODES (Designated by NUCC)

d. IS THERE ANOTHER HEALTH BENEFIT PLAN? YES [ ] NO [X] *If yes*, complete items 9, 9a, and 9d.

READ BACK OF FORM BEFORE COMPLETING & SIGNING THIS FORM.

12. PATIENT'S OR AUTHORIZED PERSON'S SIGNATURE I authorize the release of any medical or other information necessary to process this claim. I also request payment of government benefits either to myself or to the party who accepts assignment below.
SIGNED *Signature on File* DATE 06/01/2020

13. INSURED'S OR AUTHORIZED PERSON'S SIGNATURE I authorize payment of medical benefits to the undersigned physician or supplier for services described below.
SIGNED *Signature on File*

14. DATE OF CURRENT ILLNESS, INJURY, or PREGNANCY (LMP) MM 05 DD 01 YY 2020 QUAL. 431

15. OTHER DATE QUAL. MM DD YY

16. DATES PATIENT UNABLE TO WORK IN CURRENT OCCUPATION FROM MM DD YY TO MM DD YY

17. NAME OF REFERRING PROVIDER OR OTHER SOURCE
17a.
17b. NPI

18. HOSPITALIZATION DATES RELATED TO CURRENT SERVICES FROM MM DD YY TO MM DD YY

19. ADDITIONAL CLAIM INFORMATION (Designated by NUCC)

20. OUTSIDE LAB? YES [ ] NO [ ] $ CHARGES

21. DIAGNOSIS OR NATURE OF ILLNESS OR INJURY Relate A-L to service line below (24E) ICD Ind. 0
A. F43.23 B. F10.10 C. ___ D. ___
E. ___ F. ___ G. ___ H. ___
I. ___ J. ___ K. ___ L. ___

22. RESUBMISSION CODE ___ ORIGINAL REF. NO. ___

23. PRIOR AUTHORIZATION NUMBER

24. A. DATE(S) OF SERVICE From MM DD YY	To MM DD YY	B. PLACE OF SERVICE	C. EMG	D. PROCEDURES, SERVICES, OR SUPPLIES CPT/HCPCS	MODIFIER	E. DIAGNOSIS POINTER	F. $ CHARGES	G. DAYS OR UNITS	H. EPSDT Family Plan	I. ID. QUAL.	J. RENDERING PROVIDER ID. #
1	06 01 20	06 01 20	11		90791		A	150 00	1		NPI	1386652212
2	06 08 20	06 08 20	11		90837		A	120 00	1		NPI	1386652212
3	06 15 20	06 15 20	11		90847		AB	130 00	1		NPI	1386652212
4	06 20 20	06 20 20	02		90834	95	AB	110 00	1		NPI	1386652212
5											NPI	
6											NPI	

25. FEDERAL TAX I.D. NUMBER 26-1352705 SSN [ ] EIN [X]

26. PATIENT'S ACCOUNT NO.

27. ACCEPT ASSIGNMENT? (For govt. claims, see back) YES [X] NO [ ]

28. TOTAL CHARGE $ 510 00

29. AMOUNT PAID $

30. Rsvd for NUCC Use

31. SIGNATURE OF PHYSICIAN OR SUPPLIER INCLUDING DEGREES OR CREDENTIALS (I certify that the statements on the reverse apply to this bill and are made a part thereof.)
SIGNED *Barbara C. Griswold LMFT* DATE 06/20/2020

32. SERVICE FACILITY LOCATION INFORMATION
BARBARA GRISWOLD LMFT
4010 MOORPARK AVE STE 118
SAN JOSE CA 95117
a. 1386652212 b.

33. BILLING PROVIDER INFO & PH # (408) 9850846
BARBARA GRISWOLD LMFT
4010 MOORPARK AVE STE 118
SAN JOSE CA 95117
a. 1386652212 b.

NUCC Instruction Manual available at: www.nucc.org **PLEASE PRINT OR TYPE** APPROVED OMB-0938-1197 FORM 1500 (02-12)

Box	How to Compete the CMS-1500 Claim Form
Carrier Block	The carrier block is the big open white space in the upper right corner of the form, above the box for Insured's ID Number. Leave blank or enter the name and address of the insurance plan or the Payor ID number, if submitting electronically. Be sure to get the address for mental health claims (not always the same as the medical claim address on the insurance card). Enter in the following format: 1st Line – Name; 2nd Line – First line of address; 3rd Line – Second line of address (optional); 4th Line – City, State (2 characters) and ZIP code. The black square "QR" barcode on the left side of this block distinguishes this form from previous versions. The barcode can be scanned by smartphones, and will take you to www.nucc.org for more form information.
1	Identify the type of health plan with an "X". Mark only one box. Group health plans include those through an employer or group. If you aren't sure, check "other."
1 A	Enter the ID number from the client's insurance card. Include any letter prefix. Omit dashes or spaces. Use the subscriber's Social Security Number if you have no ID number.
2	The client's full name. Last name first, then a comma, then first name (and middle initial, if known). No nicknames, titles (Mr., Capt., Dr.), or professional suffixes (e.g. PhD, MD). If the patient uses a last name suffix (e.g., Jr., Sr.) enter it after the last name, and before the first name. Do not write "SAME" in this or any other field, even if the information is the same as in Item 4; the plan may think the client's last name is "SAME." With couples or families, pick an identified client for your sessions.
3	Client's 6- or 8-digit birthdate. Put an "X" in box under "sex" to indicate male or female.
4	The insured's name goes here. The insured (or subscriber) is the primary holder of the insurance – the person whose insurance the client is using. This would typically be the employee in employer-provided plans. Last name first, then a comma, then first name. No nicknames, titles, or professional suffixes. If the patient uses a last name suffix (e.g., Jr., Sr.) enter it after the last name, and before the first name. Don't write "SAME," even if the information is the same as in Item 2.
5	Client's mailing address (use two-letter state abbreviation) and phone number. P.O Boxes may not be allowed here. Do not use punctuation or symbols in the address (except hyphen if entering 9-digit ZIP). Do not use a hyphen/space to separate digits of the phone number. Do not write "SAME," even if the information is the same as Item 7.
6	How is the client related to the insured? Put an "X" in the appropriate box. "Self" means insured is the client. "Spouse" includes qualified partners, as defined by the plan. "Child" is a dependent child, as defined by the plan. If the client is a dependent but has own unique Member Identification Number, you may be able to report "Self."
7	Insured's permanent residence (use two-letter state abbreviation) and phone number. Avoid P.O Boxes. Do not use punctuation or other symbols in the address (except hyphen if entering 9-digit ZIP code). Do not use a hyphen/space to separate digits of phone number. Do not write "SAME," even if the information is the same as Item 5.
8	Leave blank, unless instructed otherwise by the insurance plan.
9 A - D	Leave blank unless client is covered by more than one insurance plan, or you are seeing a couple or family and you (or they) intend to bill two plans for the session. If so, you'll need to answer "yes" to Item 11d. In Box 9, enter information about the secondary plan. Enter the secondary insured's last name, then a comma, then first name, comma, and middle initial (name may be the same if client is double-covered). Then answer 9a and 9d as they apply to this person; leave 9b and 9c blank. Do not use hyphens/spaces in the policy or group number. Enter the name of the secondary plan, e.g. XYZ Insurance Plan. See Page 106 for more about "Double Coverage."

10 **A - C**	Mark "no" for each unless symptoms are related to a condition or injury that occurred on the job, or as a result of an accident. In these cases, mark "yes," as there may be other coverage that would be primary, such as automobile insurance or worker's compensation. If there was an auto accident, report 2-letter state abbreviation where accident occurred.
10 D	Leave blank, unless instructed otherwise by the insurance plan.
11	Fill in the group number from the insurance card. Do not use hyphens/spaces.
11 **A - C**	In 11A, enter the 6-digit or 8-digit birthdate and gender of the primary subscriber. You can leave 11B blank. For 11C identify the insurance plan type (e.g. "PPO Choice 100")
11 D	Check "yes" if the client is covered by two insurance plans, and you (or your clients) intend to bill two plans. If your response here is "yes," also complete Box 9 and 9a and 9d. Otherwise, check "no." <u>This item is a required field.</u> The provider here acknowledges having made a good faith effort to determine if there is other coverage. (For more instructions on Box 9 and "Double Coverage," see Page 106).
12	Have the client sign and date this box at least once during treatment to authorize the release to the insurance plan of any medical information necessary to process claims, and keep a copy for your files. Once you have the client's signature on file, you may write "Signature on File" on future claims. Instead of signing the claim, you may have the client sign a separate release with the same wording which you keep on file. Some therapists incorporate the wording from Box 12 into their treatment agreement and have the client sign and date that (see Sample Treatment Agreement, Page 143). If a separate release is obtained, write "Signature On File" in this box. Do not put any text in this box other than "Signature on File" or the client's signature. Parents/guardians should sign if the client is a minor.
13	If you are a network provider, or if for other reasons you want the plan to pay you, have the client sign here authorizing payment to you. As with Box 12, you may incorporate the wording from Box 13 into a treatment agreement or separate release and have the client sign and date that instead (see Sample Treatment Agreement, Page 143). If you do this, you may write "Signature on File" in this box. Parents/guardians should sign if the client is a minor. <u>Leave this box blank if you want the plan to reimburse the client directly</u> (i.e. if you use the claim form as an invoice for the client).
14	Many plans allow you to leave this box blank. If required, fill in the *estimated* 6-digit date latest symptoms began. To the right of this, you'll see "Qual" and a dashed line. Write "431" to the right of this line, indicating this is the date symptoms began (doctors use another qualifier when recording Last Menstrual Period here). ***Some plans will deny if you omit this qualifier.***
15	You may leave blank. If client has had a similar condition before, give the 6-digit date when the client had a previous related condition.
16	Leave blank, unless the client is employed but unable to work. Give the 6-or 8-digit start and end dates of time span the client was unable to work.
17	You may leave blank, unless a doctor's referral was required for treatment (rare). Enter first name, middle initial, last name and credentials of referring professional.
17 A **and B**	Leave blank, unless a doctor's referral was required for treatment. If the referring physician has a National Provider Identifier, leave this box blank, and enter the doctor's NPI in Box 17b.
18, 19, **20**	Fill out Box 18 only if the session is a result of, or subsequent to, a related hospitalization; record admission/discharge dates. Fill out Box 19 only if resubmitting a claim: Explain the reason for resubmission here (ex. "Resubmitting; Wrong POS code on original claim" and then fill out Box 22. Leave Box 20 blank, unless told otherwise.

21	Enter up to 12 diagnosis codes in priority order from the World Health Organization's *International Classification of Diseases* (ICD). Don't panic if you have never opened an ICD -- Codes in the APA's *Diagnostic and Statistical Manual* (DSM) are ICD codes. The DSM-5 lists both the old ICD-9 code followed by the current ICD-10 code for that diagnosis, in parentheses beginning with a letter (see picture). Use only ICD-10 codes for all sessions after 10/1/2015.

Panic Disorder
300.01 (F41.0)

In the upper right-hand corner of Box 21 on the form, you will see "ICD-Ind." and two vertical dashed lines. This is the ICD Indicator" where you identify which version of ICD code set you are using for diagnosis. Put a "0" (<u>NOT</u> "10") in between the two vertical dashed lines to indicate the ICD-10 is being used (see sample claim, Page 61).

<u>Important notes:</u>).
- Don't include the parentheses or the diagnosis name on the claim -- just the code.
- You will need a primary diagnosis. Many plans won't reimburse if you <u>only</u> list a relationship issue (what was called a V-code, now a Z-code in the DSM-5).
- Avoid diagnoses listed in the DSM-5 as "Unspecified" and avoid diagnoses related to sexuality. Plans may not reimburse. When possible, use alternate diagnoses.
- Be sure you have the full amount of digits for your diagnosis (3 to 7). Visit www.icd10data.com, type in your code, and look for the green triangle and the words "Billable Code" next to your code. Diagnoses codes may change yearly.
- Do not defer the diagnosis, and don't write "R/O" for "rule out."
- If a client has multiple diagnoses, report all to give the most accurate clinical picture.
- If you add a diagnosis in the billing period, include both (see Box 24E instructions).
- You may change a diagnosis during treatment, just document why in your notes.
- For diagnosis and billing for couples and families, see Chapter 17, Page 105.

For more diagnostic coding resources, see Resources, Page 133. |
22	Leave blank, unless resubmitting claims. In this case use resubmission code 7 if resubmitting a corrected claim due to an error, and 8 if you want them to cancel the prior claim. Then where it says "Original Ref. No." list the original claim number that had the mistake.
23	Write the pre-certification or authorization number(s) here, if applicable, or leave blank.
24 A	These six lines are divided, with a shaded portion on top and white portion beneath, to bill for up to six dates of service. Ignore the shaded portion, and list session dates in the white portion. For outpatient therapy, <u>list one date of service per line</u> -- either write the date in the "from" category and leave the "to" column blank, or repeat the date on each line (ex. "06/01/20 to 06/01/16"). *Dates should be in a 6 digit or 8 digit format.*
24 B	Enter the two-digit code from the Place-Of-Service Code list to indicate where the session took place, or 02 is usually required if it was a telehealth session (this varies by plan -- see Telehealth, Page 69). <u>Do not write "O," "OV" or "Office."</u> Don't use ditto marks or write "SAME" to indicate repeat information. The POS code is 11 for an office visit. *Codes change, so see Page 136 for where to get the latest Place of Service Codes.*
24 C	You may leave blank, unless directed otherwise.
24 D	Enter the AMA's Current Procedural Terminology (CPT) code for your service, identifying type of service provided. Codes don't vary by state or plan, but reimbursement and coverage varies. Authorizations may limit the codes you may bill for. Common CPT codes are on the next page. After the CPT code, there is room for four modifiers. Leave this blank, unless warranted, such as a telehealth session modifiers 95 (or sometimes GT or GQ) that may be required; see claim form Page 61, where a modifier was used in Session 4 to show the plan that this was a telehealth session. (For more on telehealth, see Page 69). Another modifier that might be used is 59, which indicates that two "separate and distinct" services took place on the same day, such as a couples session and an individual session with a client in the same day. In this case, add the 59 to the second service of the day. *(continued)*

24 D **(cont.)**	*(continued from last page)* ## CPT codes frequently used by therapists in an office setting:[32] **90791**: Psychiatric diagnostic evaluation *(plans may cover only 1 per client, sometimes 2)* **90792**: Psychiatric diagnostic evaluation w/medical services *(used by medical providers)* **90832**: Psychotherapy, 30 minutes *(for 16-37 minute sessions)* **90834**: Psychotherapy, 45 minutes *(for 38 – 52 minute sessions)* **90837**: Psychotherapy, 60 minutes *(for sessions over 53 minutes; may be seen as an extended sessions by some plans, or may not be paid routinely -- see Page 68)* **90845** Psychoanalysis **90846**: Family/couples therapy, <u>without</u> client present *(50 mins; 26 min. or more)* **90847**: Family/couples therapy, with client present *(50 min; 26 min. or longer)* **90853**: Group psychotherapy (other than multiple-family group) **90839**: Psychotherapy for crisis, first 60 minutes **90840**: Crisis code add-on code, each additional 30 minutes **90785**: Interactive complexity add-on code *(for more on this, see next page)* **A few notes:** • **90832, 90834, and 90837** may be used regardless of setting. <u>They cannot be used for ongoing couples/family therapy</u>. However, they can be used when a family member occasionally joins an ongoing individual client in session, and the individual client is present for some or all of the session, ex. when seeing a child individually and you bring in the parent(s) occasionally for part of the session. **For ongoing couples/family therapy, use 90847**. • **Add-on codes (not modifiers):** For certain codes such as crisis or interactive complexity add-on codes, they cannot be billed alone. List the original service and charge as usual on the claim; on the next line repeat the date and Place of Service code, then list the add-on code and any extra charge you choose for the increased complexity of the case. • **Examples of interactive complexity** include when using play equipment with young children, interpreters or translators, when there is high conflict among participants or caregiver that complicates treatment plan implementation, or when there is a disclosure and report of abuse/neglect. This code can only be used with diagnostic evaluations, psychotherapy, or group codes, not couples/family therapy or crisis codes. *For more on CPT coding, including for sessions over 52 minutes, see Extended Sessions, Page 68. For more CPT coding resources, see "Resources," Page 133.* *CPT codes ©American Medical Association. All rights reserved*
24 E	This box wants to know which diagnoses you treated at each session. Note the letters listed before each diagnosis in Box 21, and in Box 24E note which you treated in that session. That is, if in session #1 you focused just on the first diagnosis you listed in Box 21, write "A" in Column 24E on the line for that date of service). If you focused on more than one diagnosis in that session, enter the corresponding letters of the diagnoses, without commas between them (e.g., "AC" or "ABC"). If you look at the sample claim form on Page 61, you'll see a diagnosis was added in the third session, and is reflected by an additional letter in this column. Don't use ditto marks to indicate duplicate information. Do not write out the name of the diagnosis, or use diagnosis codes here.
24 F	Network providers: Write your normal "full" fee (not the discounted contracted rate) for the listed service -- the plan will automatically adjust it when processing the claim. Out-of-network providers: Write what was charged for the session (if you discounted your fee, reflect that here. Do not use commas, periods, or dollar signs. Don't use ditto marks.
24 G	Write number of units of service/sessions billed on that line (usually one). No ditto marks.
24 H	You may leave blank, unless otherwise indicated by the plan.

24 **I - J**	In Column I and J you will give the ID of the treating provider for each date of service. Note: In the sample claim on Page 61, it shows how to list your National Provider Identifier (NPI). **If you have an NPI,** write it in the white area of Column J next to "NPI" in Column I for each date of service (see sample claim, Page 61). Leave the shaded portion of each line blank. **If you DON'T have an NPI,** leave the white portion of each line of blank when you get to Column J I and J. Here, choose another type of approved ID number to use instead. A good option is your State License Number. In this case, for each date of service fill in the shaded upper half of Column I for the date (above the letters "NPI") with the 2-digit prefix OB, which is just a qualifier code that tells the plan that the number that follows in Column J will be your license number. In Column J, enter your license number including any letters (e.g. MFT27210) in the shaded area of each line. **If you bill electronically (via the internet) you must use an NPI.**
25	Claims must have the Tax ID Number (TIN) of the billing provider, even if you use an NPI or legacy number elsewhere on the form. Do not enter hyphens. There are two types of TINs: Social Security Numbers (SSN) or Employer Identification Numbers (EIN). I strongly recommend you get your EIN, so you don't have to use your Social Security Number on claims/invoices, to prevent identity theft. The EIN is free and easy to obtain, and you can get one even if you have no other employees (see Resources on Page 133 for where to get it). If possible, get your EIN before applying to insurance plans. If you have already been using your SSN with plans, you will need to submit an IRS W-9 form to each plan, giving them your new EIN number. Then contact health plans to be sure your EIN is on file before submitting claims under that EIN or claims may be denied. It is recommended you make your EIN effective at the beginning of the calendar year for ease of accounting.
26	If you assign clients an account number, you may record it here. Otherwise, skip this.
27	Enter an "X" in the "Yes" box if you want payment to be made to you.
28	Add the total of all individual line charges on the page. Do not use commas, periods, or dollar signs. Enter 00 in the cents area if the amount is a whole number.
29	This is where you would normally report the amount received from the client. However, if you are a network provider, you don't need to complete this section. The insurance company will calculate what it owes you without this information, and it is up to you to collect any copayments or deductibles from the client. If you are an out-of-network provider using this form as an invoice, you must enter what the client paid you. Do not use dollar signs, commas, or periods. Enter "00" if the amount is a whole number.
30	You should leave blank.
31	Sign here, including degree, credentials, or license, and date. While interns or associates typically are not reimbursed by insurance, some plans do allow this. If you have the health plan's approval, the intern/associate and supervisor should both sign, and titles such as "treating therapist" and "supervising therapist" should be used to clearly indicate roles. If unlicensed, the word "Intern" or "Associate" should be spelled out. Do not give the appearance that the unlicensed person is licensed or that the supervisor performed the therapy. Enter either the 6-digit, 8-digit, or alphanumeric date (e.g., July 20, 2020). A signature may be replaced with a computer-generated signature.
32 **&** **32** **A - B**	Enter the name and address where the services were rendered, other than the client's home. No post office boxes are allowed. Use first line for name of practice or facility, second line for address, and third line for city, state, and 9-digit ZIP. Do not use punctuation or symbols in the address, except for a hyphen in 9-digit ZIP. **If the service location is your office,** use your NPI number in Box 32a (if you have one) and skip 32b. Remember if you bill electronically you must use an NPI. *(continued)*

	(continued from last page).
32 & 32 A - B (cont)	**If you provided telehealth**, use your office address, even if you weren't there for the session. **If the service site is an agency**, use their NPI in 32a, and skip 32b. **If you or the agency does NOT have an NPI**, leave 32a blank, and in Box 32b give a non-NPI number. I recommend you simply use your state license number. Before your license number you'll need a 2-digit "qualifier" code prefix that identifies the type of non-NPI ID number you are using. For example, the qualifier prefix OB indicates that the next series of letters and numbers to follow are your state license, and might look like OBMFT27210.
33 & 33 A - B	Here's where you tell them who the check should be made out to, and where it should be sent. Include your degree or license, if applicable. Put your name (or the facility's) on the top line, address on second, and City, State and ZIP on bottom line. Do not use punctuation or symbols, except hyphens with a 9-digit ZIP. It is OK if your billing address is not the same as your service address. Enter your phone number in the upper right portion of the box; do not use a hyphen as a separator within the phone number. **If the billing provider/facility has a National Provider Identifier (NPI)**, write it in Box 33a, and skip 33b. Note: if you bill electronically (via the Internet), an NPI must be used. **If the billing provider does not have an NPI**, skip 33a, and in 33b give a non-NPI as you did in 32b. I recommend you use a state license number: Put the 2-digit "qualifier" code prefix that identifies the type of non-NPI ID number you are using in front of your license number. For example, the qualifier prefix OB indicates that the letters and numbers to follow are your state license, and might look like OBMFT27210. Don't use a hyphen between the prefix and the legacy number. If your client was seen at a facility or group, and the facility or group is billing for the service, use their NPI or non-NPI legacy number, not yours.

Adapted from instructions in the National Uniform Claim Committee's Claim Form Instruction Manual[33]

A Few General Claims Tips

- ▶ **Document the date you submitted the claim.** Keep a copy of paper claims submitted.

- ▶ **About the Coordination of Benefits form (COB):** On this form, the client confirms there is no other coverage that might be primary. For example, if Jack is employed, but you are billing Jill's plan, her plan might be curious why Jack's plan isn't footing the bill. The COB form is available from the plan. For more on "double coverage," see Page 106.

- ▶ **If you make errors on a claim and need to file a new corrected claim:** In Box 19 on the CMS-1500 Form, explain the reason for the resubmission (ex. "Reprocess: Incorrect CPT code on claim") and in Box 22 write a 7 to indicate it is a replacement claim. In Box 22 under "Original Ref. No." put the original claim number of the claim you are correcting.

- ▶ **Do all plans accept CMS-1500s?** Most do. Some Employee Assistance Programs may require that their own billing forms be used.

- ▶ **For network providers, claims may be denied if submitted more than 60 or 90 days after the session.** Most contracts won't allow you to bill the client for late-filed claims. You can try filing an appeal. If you had a good reason, such as illness or emergency situation, the plan may take pity on you and pay it.

- ▶ **Sessions from two separate calendar years** should be split into separate claims.

- ▶ **Will the insurance plan reimburse for time spent doing paperwork?** I wish!

Billing for "Extended Sessions"

Therapists who offer sessions of longer than 50 minutes were left high and dry in 2013 when the American Medical Association overhauled the CPT codes and deleted codes for 75-80 minute sessions. As of this writing, there are only three, timed, individual psychotherapy codes, the longest one being 90837 for 60 minutes. With instructions to use the 90837 code for all sessions longer than 52 minutes, this meant there was no way to distinguish a 53-minute session from a two- or three-hour session. Thus, reimbursement is typically based on the 60-minute rate. Providers should inform clients that their reimbursement may be limited due to this.

While many plans do allow ongoing, routine 60-minute sessions, and even pay more than for the 45-minute code, the largest health plan in the country, United Behavioral Health/OPTUM/United Healthcare, does not support the use of regular 60-minute sessions. This plan considers these to be "extended sessions," and only authorizes the use of extended sessions in special circumstances, such as for EMDR, systematic desensitization, or intense trauma-informed treatment for PTSD. As always, it's a good idea to contact the plan in advance to check their coverage of 90837.

If the session meets criteria for a crisis session, consider using the crisis codes 90839 (the first 60 minutes of a crisis session) and 90840 add-on (for each 30 minutes of time after a 90839).

It is not usually recommended that you break the session into two parts and bill separately for each (ex. a 90834 and a 90832 on the same day). However, one provider did tell me that she was successfully reimbursed by an insurance plan when she did a 120 min session and billed 2 units of 90837. Most clients, though, only are covered for one 45- or 60-minute session per day.

Let's say you do a two-hour session. Can a network provider bill the plan for a 60-minute session, and contract privately with the client to pay the other 60 minutes out of pocket? If your contract does not forbid this, I believe that this should be acceptable, since clients retain the right to purchase more services than their insurance will cover. I spoke to the Senior Provider Relations Manager at two different health plans, who said they felt it was not a contract violation, as long as the client had signed something in advance like my Private Pay Agreement (see Sample Page 149), stating he understood that this additional time would be his financial responsibility, what the cost would be, and that insurance won't be billed. Be sure to collect only the copay and any deducible for the part of the session billed to insurance, and charge only your network rate for the additional time.

Prolonged Services Codes: A final billing possibility for individual sessions of at least 90 minutes emerged in 2016 when the AMA allowed Prolonged Services add-on codes, 99354 and 99355, to be used by therapists along with 90837 sessions.[34] Then in 2018, these were allowed with CPT code 90847 couples and family sessions at least 80 minutes long.[35] Formerly allowed to be used only by medical professionals, these "add-on codes" can be used when billing for services that have gone on longer than the usual time. Billing requires use of multiple CPT codes and multiple claim lines for the same session, with your assigned charges for each. For example:

INDIVIDUAL THERAPY:

For 90 – 134 minute sessions, you would bill:
    90837 (first 60 minutes), and also
    99354 (30 – 74 minutes following the initial 90837)

For 135 – 164 minute sessions, you would bill:
    90837 (first 60 minutes), and also
    99354 (30 – 74 minutes following the initial 90837), and also
    99355 (each additional 30 minutes; must be used with 99354)

For 165 – 194 minute sessions, you would bill:
    90837 (first 60 minutes), and also
    99354 (30 – 74 minutes following the initial 90837), and also
    99355 (each additional 30 minutes; must be used with 99354), and also
    99355 (each additional 30 minutes; must be used with 99354)

FAMILY/COUPLES THERAPY:

> **For 80 – 124 minute sessions, you would bill:**
>> 90847 (first 50 minutes), and also
>> 99354 (30 – 74 minutes following the initial 90847)

> **For 125 – 154 minute sessions, you would bill:**
>> 90847 (first 50 minutes), and also
>> 99354 (30 – 74 minutes following the initial 90847), and also
>> 99355 (each additional 30 minutes; must be used with 99354)

> **For 155 – 184 minute sessions, you would bill:**
>> 90847 (first 50 minutes), and also
>> 99354 (30 – 74 minutes following the initial 90847), and also
>> 99355 (each additional 30 minutes; must be used with 99354), and also
>> 99355 (each additional 30 minutes; must be used with 99354)

Again, notice that couples and family sessions have different time thresholds than individual therapy, since 90847 and 90837 have different time lengths (50 and 60 min, respectively). The maximum number of 99355 codes that can be used for one day is four.

But, will insurance pay for Prolonged Service codes? Some therapists who used these codes have been reimbursed for the extra time, others only got paid only for the initial 90837 or 90847. Before using these codes, it is recommended that you verify coverage with the plan.

Telehealth: Billing for Video or Phone Sessions

First, a disclaimer: The topic of telehealth is so large and complex, I can't cover it all here. In these pages, I will focus only on basic billing and coverage questions.

Let's start by defining terms: The terms "telemedicine" or "telehealth" are often used interchangeably and informally when referring to "synchronous" (live two way) communication, such as phone or video sessions. However, the definition varies between federal programs, state laws, and insurance plans. When dealing with coverage questions, know whether the definition includes telephone sessions and/or "asynchronous communication" (ex. text, email, provider portal messages). When I use the term "telehealth" in this chapter, I'll be referring to video and phone sessions. Text or email conversations with clients typically are not covered.

Perhaps you noticed the explosion? The biggest change in the field of therapy over the last decade has been the dramatic expansion of treatment via video and phone. While telehealth sessions were slowly increasing in popularity each year prior to 2020, nothing could have prepared us for the explosion of telehealth early that year. The COVID-19 pandemic led to worldwide shelter-in-place orders, leaving both therapists and clients unable to leave their homes. This forced even the most hesitant among us to move our practices online, or at least consider telehealth as a means to continue to provide services. The number of therapists online skyrocketed almost overnight, at times overwhelming the capacity of online platforms to handle them. If therapists or clients could not do video sessions, phone sessions became the new normal.

But was telehealth covered before the pandemic? Prior to the pandemic, telehealth psychotherapy sessions were not covered by a large number of major insurance plans. However, as mentioned, there has been a steady shift toward laws that mandate telehealth coverage. As of July 2019, 36 states and the District of Colombia required private insurance plans to cover telehealth coverage if the service would be covered in-person (also known as "coverage parity"). 21 states and the District of Columbia required coverage parity for Medicaid telehealth sessions.[36]

However, even when telehealth was covered by insurance plans, coverage conditions were often imposed. Preauthorization might have been needed. The plan might only allow it when there were no network providers available near the client, or none with the necessary specialty or language capability. The therapist might have to be in-network, be on the plan's telehealth provider list, and/or have attested to a knowledge of state telehealth laws. Most health plans didn't cover phone sessions. The client might have had to sign a special telehealth informed consent, and/or have had an in-person intake (for my Telehealth Informed consent, see my Practice Forms Packet at Resources, Page 133).

And what's changed with COVID? While many insurance plans had previously been slow to cover telehealth, as of March, 2020, almost all plans began encouraging and covering telehealth to discourage the spread of the COVID-19 virus. Many plans relaxed their previous limitations. Some are allowed telehealth for psychotherapy sessions, and some began allowing out-of-network providers to provide this service to current clients. Most allowed phone sessions and dropped pre-authorization requirements. In fact, a large number of plans waived client copayments for telehealth sessions, even for mental health. However, several plans still say they have some conditions, such as needing the therapist to be on a telehealth provider list, or to be in-network.

What CPT code should be used for telehealth sessions? Use the same 5-digit CPT code you would have used if the client was seen in person. Yes, even for phone sessions.

Then, how will the plan know the session was not in-person? Most plans will require that your CPT code be followed by a telehealth modifier, usually 95, or the older modifier GT. Some plans don't need a modifier, others will accept either 95 or GT. These modifiers are entered in the box just to the right of your CPT codes on the CMS-1500 claim form (Column 24D). It is recommended you check with the plan to see which modifier they want you to use. If you can't get through to the plan, and the pandemic is still in full swing when you are reading this, read my article at www.theinsurancemaze.com/coronavirus for information on general plan-by-plan temporary telehealth coverage.

What about the Place of Service Code? In Column 24B of the CMS-1500 form, you will usually need to put 02, which as of 2017 is the code for a telehealth session. However, Medicare and some private plans as of this writing want you to use the Place of Service code you would have used if the session was in-person (e.g. 11 for office). So avoid making assumptions.

What if I'm an out-of-network provider? The codes are the same. Statements should clearly identify telehealth sessions by using these codes; it is fraud to bill for a telehealth session in a way that would give the impression that it was face-to-face. I advise out-of-network providers to add two columns on their statement to record Place of Service code and modifiers, as these are important to highlight if you provide telehealth (see Sample Invoice on Page 145). It's also a good idea to have a session description to make it clear that the session was provided via phone or video (e.g. "45 min. therapy session, video"). Having said all this, remember: Not all health plans cover telehealth with out-of-network providers, or if they do, they may not waive the client's coinsurance even if they are waiving it for clients who see network providers.

How do I find out if my client's insurance covers telehealth? Unfortunately, coverage information on a plan's website or portal doesn't always contain telehealth coverage details. The most reliable way to find out if a client has telehealth coverage is still to call their plan. E-mailing the plan with questions may work with some plans. You should provide the client's name, date of birth, and health plan ID number, even when asking general coverage questions. This is because coverage may vary depending on your state or the client's employer account, and whether it is a group or individual plan. Some plans (e.g. ERISA or self-insured plans) have different rules and are not obligated to follow state laws.

What should I ask the plan when I call? Use the Checking Coverage form on Page 41. In addition to the usual questions, you should ask if video sessions are covered for the CPT code you are providing. Also ask about phone sessions, in case of unexpected video connection issues. Ask if there are any conditions. Ask what Place of Service code and modifier is needed, if any.

Will plans pay the same as in-person sessions? In most cases, yes. But only 16 states mandate payment parity for private payers, requiring that the rate paid by private plans for telehealth be the same as for an in-person visit, while 28 states have Medicaid payment parity mandates.[37]

Does my documentation change? In general, your documentation should be the same as for in-person sessions, with the addition of a Telehealth Consent, and a Credit Card Authorization, if applicable. However, you should also document that at the start of each telehealth session you asked the client to confirm his exact location, in case of emergency. If the session is by phone, you should also document that you verified the client's identity. Document in each progress note whether the session was a video or phone session. Be sure you have an updated emergency contact on file, and that you are aware of emergency resources where the client is located. Insurance plans may check to be sure you have written telehealth policies and consents as well as emergency procedures on file.

What online telehealth platform must I use? I strongly suggest that you choose a HIPAA-compatible and secure online platform (some plans have required it). However, as you may have read, on 3/17/20, the U.S. Dept of Health and Human Services temporarily waived enforcement of HIPAA regulations related to telehealth platforms during this health emergency, stating that "covered health care providers may use popular applications that allow for video chats, including Apple FaceTime, Facebook Messenger video chat, Google Hangouts video, or Skype, to provide telehealth" without risking that the government might impose a penalty.[38]

Recommendations before you provide telehealth: Get all clients to sign your telehealth consent and credit card authorization (you can send these via secure email or mail). Then get training. Learn about the subtle legal and ethical obligations when the client is at a distance, as well as how to handle clinical and technological challenges, and policies you should have in place. These include how to handle an emergencies, technology problems, and how to handle confidentiality issues.

What if my client doesn't have telehealth coverage? If the client has a health-related savings account, he may be able to use his HSA/MSA/FSA balance to pay for telehealth (see Page 11 for more on these accounts). Otherwise, plans typically will allow you to bill a client directly for this service, since it is not a covered service, if he has signed an agreement in advance to pay (see Sample Private Pay Agreement, Page 149).

Can I provide telehealth across state lines? Here's the short answer to a complex question: In general, you cannot provide telehealth services to a client unless you are licensed in the state where the client is at the time of service, unless you get approval from the licensing board in the other state. During COVID many states waived the need for this pre-approval, but you'll need to check. There are certain exceptions, such as providing emergency response to a client in another state.

Will insurance cover phone support between sessions? Not usually. One case manager told me the fee paid for sessions included any telephone calls made to (or for) the client outside the session. "You will have some clients that need a lot of phone time, some that require little or none," she explained. "The fee we pay is an average of both."

How will telehealth be covered in the future? This remains to be seen. You'll need to check back with a client's health plan to see when their temporary coverage expires, and what the new coverage terms will be. As I write this, we are in the midst of the pandemic. It is impossible to know how long the plans will continue to cover phone or video sessions, and waive copayments. While I do predict most therapists will return to in-person sessions when the pandemic is over, I do believe we will see a large number of therapists continuing to provide telehealth as part of their practice, and many move to an all-telehealth practice. I also believe that COVID-19 will have had the effect of boosting telehealth coverage in many plans, even after the pandemic is over.

(For Telehealth Resources see Resources starting on Page 133; Practice Forms Packet on Page 133 has Telehealth Agreement).

Claim Questions and Answers

I'm an out-of-network provider, and my client pays me in full. What kind of invoice do I give?

You have three choices for giving invoices to out of network clients: 1) You can give an invoice to the client (see Sample Invoice Page 145 for what to include), which he submits to the plan. Your client will need to attach your invoice to a billing form obtained from his employer or health plan. 2) You can have him fill out the top half of the CMS-1500 form to submit with your invoice. Or 3) you can fill out the entire CMS-1500 form, leave Box 13 blank, check "No" in Box 27, and put the amount he paid in Box 29. There is also a smartphone app called Reimbursify that clients can use to upload your invoices to their health plan, by taking a picture of the invoice.

Occasionally the plan will ask out-of-network providers for an IRS W-9 form before they will process the claim. This form is downloadable from the Internal Revenue Service website. The W-9 verifies your Tax Identification Number. I suggest you get a free Employer ID you can use instead of your Social Security Number on all invoices (For more on the EIN, see Page 66, Box 25).

I am not a network provider. But if my client can't afford my full fee, and has out-of-network benefits, can I collect his coinsurance, and bill the plan for the rest?

It is risky. First, some plans cut the check to a client, no matter what you put on the claim form. If this happens, it may be hard to get Jack to pay you, especially if he has left therapy. Second, it may be hard to know how much to collect from him at each session, since the plan may not tell you their allowed amount --or UCR -- up front, if there is one (more on UCRs, Page 40).

I bill by mail. Do I have to fill out a new CMS-1500 form every time I bill?

While electronic billing is highly preferred, a few therapists I know simply fill out most of the form by hand after the first session, leaving the session-specific information blank, to use as a reusable template. However, insurance plans highly prefer that you use original red CMS-1500 forms (not downloaded or copied forms). These are usually paid much more quickly, since only these can be computer-scanned. There is a trend away from accepting handwritten claims; some plans now require original red paper claims be completed by form-filling software (see Resources, Page 133).

What about no-shows or late-cancelled sessions? Can I bill insurance or the client?

Most insurance companies will not cover missed sessions. Contact the plan or check your contract for their policy on missed sessions. Some EAPs pay for missed sessions, most don't. With some EAPs, the member may lose one free session for each no-show. Medicaid plans don't cover no-shows, and don't allow you to bill clients. Don't bill the plan unless you know they reimburse for missed sessions. Clearly indicate that it was a missed session on the claim form or invoice.

As to whether you can charge the client for the missed session, contracts vary on this issue. Most insurance companies allow you to bill only if the client has agreed in advance (and in writing) to pay for missed sessions. Have a line devoted to this in your treatment agreement (see Sample Treatment Agreement, Page 143). <u>You are only able to charge your discounted contracted rate</u>.

How often do I need to bill insurance?

I suggest submitting claims after Session #1, then at least twice monthly, to find out early about coverage issues. As was stated, plans may not pay network providers if the claim is received more than 60 or 90 days after the session. Check regularly to see if you've been paid for all submitted claims. Call all your clients' plans before the first January session -- many benefits change in January.

How long should I wait before I call the insurance plan if I haven't been paid?

This varies by plan. Blue Cross says to wait 30 working days for PPO plans and 45 working days for HMO plans. Many plan websites allow you to track claim status. If they say they didn't receive it, they may ask you to resubmit the claim. Or you can ask if you can fax the new claim, to expedite processing. Document the call date, who you spoke to, what they said, the confirmation number, and actions taken.

12

The Check Arrives — or Doesn't
Explanation of Benefits and Denials

ಊ ಆ

Weeks after submitting your claim for Jack's sessions, the mail carrier brings the monthly bill for the gym you aren't attending – and an envelope from CureQuick. Before you dance on your desk, you open the CureQuick envelope and look closely at the paperwork you've received.

Inside the envelope you find an Explanation of Benefits (EOB) like the one below. An EOB outlines how the claim was processed, shows deductions made for copayments, co-insurance, or deductibles, and shows the final net payment to you or the client. If you have not signed up for automatic payments into your bank account, and the charges didn't go toward the client's deductible, a check should be attached. A copy of the EOB is also sent to the policy holder; this may not be the client. Below is a sample EOB; on the next page we'll discuss it in detail.

 CureQuick Behavioral Health
788 Paper Street Suite 118
Paper Trail, MN 55344
800-555-1234

EXPLANATION OF BENEFITS

ISSUE DATE	CHECK NUMBER
June 30, 2020	0002795220

Control Number 0010388563
Provider Tax ID   26-1352705
CUREQUICK VENDOR ID: 67750

BARBARA GRISWOLD, LMFT
4010 MOORPARK AVE. #118
SAN JOSE, CA   95117

Patient Name: KLUTZ, JACK   ID Number: PRU34567-00 Acct. Nbr: 90 Group: HOO123
Claim ID: 05222451522   Claim Received: 06/24/20   CUREQUICK BH AGREEMENT

Service Date	Procedure Code	Billed Amount	Not Allowed	Allowed Amount	Deductible	Co-insurance/ Copayment	Claims Payment
06/01/20	90791	150.00	55.00 / 01	95.00		19.00	76.00
06/08/20	90837	120.00	30.00 / 01	90.00		18.00	72.00
06/15/20	90847	130.00	45.00 / 01	85.00		17.00	68.00
06/22/20	90834	110.00	30.00 / 01	80.00		16.00	64.00
TOTALS:		**510.00**	**160.00**	**350.00**		**70.00**	**280.00**

01 – This is the amount in excess of the allowed expense for a participating provider. The member, therefore, is not responsible for this amount.

Understanding the EOB

Why did you get paid only $280.00 when you submitted a bill for $510? For the first session, $55 of your $150 fee was "not allowed" since in this example your contracted rate for an intake session (CPT code 90791) is $95. In our example, Jack's co-insurance (the percentage of the contracted rate that he is responsible to pay) is 20 percent, so he is responsible for 20 percent of your contracted rate of $95, or $19. CureQuick paid the rest (Note: many plans like CureQuick pay a higher reimbursement rate for an intake session).

For session two, $30 of your fee was not allowed, since your contracted rate for an individual 60-minute session (CPT code 90837) is $90. Jack paid his co-insurance, which is 20 percent of $90, or $18.00. CureQuick paid the rest ($72.00).

In the third session, you'll notice from the CPT code that it was a couples or family session. $85 is your contracted rate for a couples therapy session, so the $45 difference between this amount and your $130 fee was not allowed. Jack paid his 20 percent of your $85 contracted rate, or $17, and CureQuick paid the balance ($68). Note that some plans pay more --- and some pay less -- for a couples or family session than for a 60-minute individual session.

In the fourth session, $30 was not allowed, since $80 is your contracted rate for an individual 45-minute session (CPT code 90834). The client paid his 20 percent copay ($16), and the plan paid the rest ($64).

There may be a code footnoted below the chart, reminding you why that amount was not allowed. In this case, this reminds you as a plan provider you have discounted your rate, and that you can't collect this "not allowed" amount from the client. This would be "balance-billing," which is prohibited when you have a contract. You must accept your contracted rate as payment in full.

What to Do When You Get the EOB

▶ **Check it for accuracy.** Underpayments often go unnoticed. Be sure the right amount of provider discount, copayment and/or deductible was taken out, and that you have been paid the rest.

▶ **If it was an EAP session, be sure the claim was paid in full.** The insurance plan may have underpaid you, processing it as a normal mental health visit, taking out a copayment.

▶ **If the insurance company has overpaid you, call.** The insurance company may have paid more than it should have for a session, or paid for the same session twice. While it's tempting not to report an overpayment, if you don't, sometimes the plan may recognize their mistake down the line and ask you for a refund – after you've already spent it. If you don't refund them, the owed amount may be taken out of future reimbursement checks for other plan clients. Remember also that it is insurance fraud to accept an overpayment, and could put your license in jeopardy. The plans often will send a written request for refund, if they notice their error.

▶ **If you believe you've been underpaid, call.** You can sometimes get it cleared up quickly on the phone. As always, document the call and representative's name.

► **Different claims address?** Don't lose sleep if the insurance company address on the EOB is different from the address where you mailed the claim. Claims are often received and paid at different locations.

► **Record insurance payments in Jack's chart and in your accounting books,** noting the date paid, check number, and the dates of service and clients each check covered (see Sample Service Record, Page 147). Then place the EOB in the chart.

Questions and Answers

Jack has a $250 deductible. Why didn't any of this go toward the deductible?

One of Jack's other providers (or Jack) may have previously submitted claims that satisfied his deductible. Or with Jack's plan the deductible may be waived if he sees a network provider.

How long does it take to be reimbursed?

It varies by health plan, and depends on how you submit the bill. In my experience, it usually averages four to six weeks for the checks to roll in if you mail the claims, but only two to four weeks if submitted electronically through a clearinghouse or at the plan's website.

If you do not receive an EOB within six weeks, your claim (or payment) may have gone astray, so call the insurance plan. Many insurance companies allow you to check claim status any time of the day by automated phone service or at their provider website. Because there are filing deadlines, it is important to following up in a timely fashion to allow time to resubmit claims, if needed.

What if an EOB combines payments for several clients? How do I file this?

CureQuick may list payments for Jack and another CureQuick client on the same EOB. It is important not to file this form in either client's chart, as this would be a HIPAA Privacy violation. The EOB lists private health information of another client, whose confidentiality could be compromised if filed in Jack's chart, where the record could be viewed by Jack or a third party who has access to Jack's chart. You can try to separate the portions of the EOB that refer to each client, or redact any information about the other client, and file them in each client's chart. I actually file these "multiple payment" EOBs in a separate file cabinet, filed by the insurance company name.

My client doesn't want her husband to know she is in therapy, but she is using his insurance. Will the EOB come addressed to him?

Unfortunately, yes. Copies of EOBs and treatment authorizations are usually mailed to the name and address on record for the primary subscriber (in this case, your client's husband). This is a problem that to my knowledge has not been addressed. Your client may want to call the insurance plan to see if there is anything they can do. She may reconsider whether she wants to use his insurance. Or she might want to try to beat him to the mailbox. Most importantly for you, it is a topic worth bringing up in therapy with her.

I'm an out-of-network provider, and I offered to collect my client's coinsurance only and submit the bill for him. Why didn't the insurance plan pay the rest of my fee?

It can be risky not to get full payment from your client as an out-of-network provider; for more about this, see Page 72. As for why the plan didn't pay in full, they probably subtracted any deductible, and/or paid only their portion for out-of-network providers. Remember, plans may put a cap on what they will pay – often called the "Usual, Customary and Reasonable (UCR)" fee or "Allowed Amount." This is the maximum the plan will allow for the service, given your degree, license and geographical area. For a client with a 50% out of network coinsurance, the maximum reimbursement will be 50% of this Allowed Amount -- which may be less than your fee. The good news? As an out-of-network provider, you can (and should) now bill the client for any unpaid portion of your fee -- it is fraud to bill the plan for a fee that you do not attempt to collect.

Why did I get an EOB with an interest payment?

Plans may be required to pay interest to providers if they do not process claims in a timely fashion. Once I got interest when the plan continuously turned down my claims saying I didn't have an authorization on file, when I had one. Another time a claim was paid with an interest payment, explaining "interest is due when claims are paid over 30 business days after the claim date of receipt. A claim paid more than 30 business days after receipt accrues 15 percent annual interest each day until the claim is paid. An additional amount of $10 per claim may be included if applicable penalty payment rules apply."

Why Your Claim Might be Denied

Perhaps everything sounded fine when you checked coverage. But once you submit the claim, it is denied. When this happens, the Explanation of Benefits should list a reason. But the listed reason for denial is often not the actual reason, or isn't clear. While you can't always trust the EOB, it is sometimes accurate. A few reasons why your claim might be denied include:

▶ **Diagnosis issues.** Most likely you have given an old diagnosis. Each year, diagnoses are updated. Use www.icd10data.com and look for a green triangle next to your chosen diagnosis to see if it acceptable. You may not have used the full number of digits necessary (ex. F42 when you need it to be F42.2). You may have put both ICD-9 and ICD-10 diagnoses on the claim, or used the parentheses. It is also possible that you used a non-covered diagnosis; avoid diagnoses with the word "Unspecified" in them, and sexual disorders, as these may not be covered by some plans. Finally, insurance typically requires more than just a Z-code diagnosis.

▶ **If needed, no authorization was found** in place for the date of the session you claimed. While in my experience, most plans no longer require preauthorization, some plans need this before the first session, others require it after a certain number of sessions each year, and EAPs will require this). It is also possible that your authorization may have expired by the date of the session, or you may have already exceeded the number of allotted sessions.

▶ **CPT code issues.** You billed for a type of service other than the ones that were authorized, used a code they do not cover, or used a non-existent or old code (for more on CPT codes, see Page 64 to 65).

▶ **Wrong place-of-service code.** For example, under "Place of Service," you may have written "O," "OV," "OFF" or "Office" to stand for office, instead of the required "11" (for "office"). For a telehealth session, you may have put 11, when most plans require the 02 telehealth POS code (though some want an 11 here -- see Telehealth, Page 69). Or you may have used the wrong code, or one they will not reimburse for (see Resources, Page 133 for where to get codes).

▶ **Telephone or online therapy sessions were denied because** this is not a covered benefit under the clients plan, you weren't on the plan's authorized telehealth provider list, or perhaps they cover only telehealth with network providers, and you are out of network.

▶ **You are not a network provider**, and the plan doesn't reimburse for out-of-network providers (this would occur with HMOs or EPOs).

▶ **Missing EOB from primary insurance.** If you are billing the secondary health plan, you should have attached the EOB from the primary (see Double Coverage, Chapter 17).

▶ **Déjà vu.** You have previously billed for this date of service, and it is a duplicate claim.

▶ **The client has exceeded yearly benefits.** Since most plans now allow unlimited sessions, this is rare. However, for plans that have annual limits, this is an issue. If you feel the client is in need of more sessions, you may want to contact the plan to discuss options.

▶ **The claim was late.** Most plans require network providers to submit claims no more than 60 or 90 days after the date of service. If you are late, - the plan will not allow you to bill the client for your error (you may be able to appeal -- see Chapter 13).

▶ **The claim was not submitted to the correct address.** Always check the claims address by calling the plan before submission! Don't trust the claim address on the EOB, the health plan card, or the one given by the automated phone service at the health plan, as it is often the address for medical claims only, out-of-date, different, or just plain wrong.

▶ **You submitted the incorrect claim form or neglected to include the required documents.** EAPs may not accept a CMS-1500. Or plans may require the latest version of the CMS-1500 and you submitted an older version. Some companies (EAPs especially) might require that you send along a closed case form before they will pay. Out-of-network providers might be asked to send W-9 forms to attest to their Tax ID. This is normal -- go ahead and do it.

▶ **The provider was an intern or associate, and the plan doesn't cover unlicensed providers.**

▶ **The claim was incomplete or illegible.**

▶ **The claim is being held, or "pended," awaiting further information** needed to process the claim. Frequently, a claim is pended awaiting information from the member about "coordination of benefits." This is when the plan wants to find out if the client is covered by another health plan that should be responsible for primary payment of the claim (for more on coordination of benefits, see Page 67, and "Double Coverage," Page 106).

What to Do if Your Claim is Denied

Breathe. Count to ten. Meditate. Perhaps a little yoga stretching. Then keep reading for ideas on what to do next.

13

Appeals
Fighting Denials

ೲ ಛ

The Explanation of Benefits comes in the mail for your sessions with Jack. However, no matter how hard you shake the envelope, the expected reimbursement check does not fall out. Upon closer inspection, you see the charges were denied. Or perhaps after a treatment review, Jack's case manager says she want to review the case, since she doesn't believe they are medically necessary. What do you do?

The 10 Rules of Successful Telephone Calls to the Plan

1. **A phone call should be your first response.** It often allows for a better understanding of the reason for the denial and speeds up the resolution.

2. **Have the client's chart in front of you.** Take time to review the case before calling. Have the client's date of birth, ID number, dates of service, total amount billed, claim number, and other relevant information.

3. **If the issue involves medical necessity, prepare!** You might want to review the plan's medical necessity guidelines (often part of the provider manual, which may be available on the plan's website), and Chapter 9 of this book. Ask for a list of questions you'll be asked about the case -- they will often share it in advance. Jot down some notes about your treatment plan, the client's current symptoms, functioning, impairments, medications, progress, remaining treatment goals, and planned interventions.

4. **Put aside 20 to 30 minutes for the phone call.** You may have to be put on hold, get transferred, and talk to several people at the plan in some detail. You don't want to hang up frustrated with the matter unresolved, and have to call again.

5. **Take a deep breath.** Use one of those relaxation techniques you teach your clients, and get into your "happy place."

6. **Be friendly, stay calm, and avoid defensiveness.** Remember: The plan employees are not your enemy. They are just doing their job.

7. **Be specific about what you want.** Don't whine about the health plan or insurance plan as a whole. While I'm sure whatever you are upset about is *completely* valid, the wrong attitude can quickly alienate those who are in a position to help you.

8. **When talking to a case manager, speak to her as a peer, which may be the case.** An increasing number of case managers are licensed clinicians. Assume that the case manager simply knows less about the client's situation than you do, and with some additional enlightenment, s/he might share your view about the case.

9. **Avoid anything that might be interpreted as a threat, or overly dramatic predictions** that your client will decompensate or commit suicide if your appeal is not granted. However, it is fair to make objective clinical predictions of negative consequences if therapy is decreased or cut off.

10. **As always, keep a communication log.** Record the names of all those you speak with, dates and times of conversations, what they say, and call confirmation numbers.

Steps to Appealing a Denial

▶ **Call the health plan. But who do you talk to?**

1. **Claims issues:** Call the Claims Department or Customer Service. They can often quickly identify their errors on the phone, and promise to resubmit the claims for reprocessing. At other times, they help you identify *your* error, and you can resubmit the claim. If you need to send a corrected claim, follow the directions on Page 67. Ask the plan if there is a way to expedite this (ex. a fax number you can send it to). If you are an out-of-network provider resubmitting a corrected invoice, clearly indicate that it is a "corrected invoice" and identify the type of correction so the invoice isn't denied as a duplicate. If the plan rep has agreed to resubmit a claim for reprocessing, ask her to read to you the notes she has written about your case. Ask how long to allow for reprocessing, and mark this date on your calendar to follow-up if you haven't heard from them.

2. **Treatment, authorization, or medical necessity issues:** Call the case management department -- you may need to schedule a telephone interview with a care manager. Take time before you pick up the phone to put together a reasoned, clinical, non-defensive argument for why you believe the services are medically necessary (see Chapter 9 for more on this important concept). Key concepts: Be sure the treatment is alleviating medical symptoms (like anxiety, insomnia, depression) and be able to discuss how treatment has shown to be effective, and why the need for treatment still exists.

▶ **If you have to leave a message,** leave as much identifying information as possible. This may include your name -- spelled out slowly -- your area code and phone number (repeated once), the client's name -- spelled out slowly -- and date of birth, the policyholder's name and ID number, and date of birth (if client is not the policyholder), and details about your problem (See Page 29 for tips and a sample script). If it is a claim issue, include the date(s) of service in question, the amount you charged, and the claim number, if you have it.

▶ **If necessary, ask to speak to a supervisor.** Supervisors may have the power to make exceptions to company policy, or may be more knowledgeable about plans, parity laws, or higher-level claim issues. They may also assist if you have a complaint about a plan representative. However, you may not be able to bypass a lower-level representative; usually a supervisor will not speak with you unless you have discussed the issues first with someone lower on the hierarchy.

▶ **Ask for a phone appointment to speak to the plan's medical director or clinical director.** If you have spoken to the case manager and supervisor and have been unable to resolve a treatment disagreement, you may choose this option. When I spoke to a medical director it was a very positive conversation. He had the power to overrule the case manager's decision, and my request was fulfilled.

▶ **After talking to your client, submit a written appeal.** If you cannot get the matter resolved by phone, you or your client may use the health plan's formal appeal or dispute resolution process. An appeal or dispute is where you formally request that the health plan reconsider a treatment denial or a claim denial. You may also use this process to ask for an exception to the insurance plan's policies. **A sample appeal letter can be found on Page 84**. Treatment appeals are then reviewed at the health plan by another clinician, a plan psychiatrist, and/or the plan's appeals committee. You may ask for an expedited appeal if you need immediate approval to continue necessary treatment.

If this is in reference to a denied claim, a letter outlining the plan's appeal and dispute procedure should have come with the denied claim. Contact the insurance plan for more details about its appeal process, what to include in your letter, and where to submit it. Be sure to file your appeal in a timely fashion. Most insurance companies require that you submit it within a certain time period (e.g., 60 days) of the denial. Many plans have appeal forms and instructions on their websites.

As always, focus on why the treatment is the most clinically effective and cost-effective. Include a copy of the EOB if it was a claim denial, or any relevant clinical information and documentation with your request for reconsideration of a treatment denial. Your client may have the right to receive, upon written request and for free, information the insurance plan used to review the initial claim or treatment request. This information can assist in an appeal. Revisit Chapter 9 for ideas to help with this letter if the denial involved medical necessity. You may want to hire an insurance consultant to help you craft a persuasive appeal letter (see Resources, Page 133).

▶ **Contact your professional organization.** They can often give you advice on how to challenge a denial, or which section of law to cite when appealing.

▶ **Contact your state's Department of Insurance** (and/or the state's Department of Managed Health Care, if you have one in your state -- see Appendix A, Page 129). While you can always call for advice, most states want you to have utilized the health plan's internal dispute resolution process before filing a complaint at the state. However, if your appeal with the plan is denied, or if you have not received a timely response, filing a complaint with the state is appropriate. In my opinion, it is an under-utilized tool therapists should use more often to get needed payment or treatment.

When a health plan is denying, delaying, or modifying a service or service frequency because it does not believe the service is medically necessary, or they feel it is experimental, or won't cover an emergency service already provided, you may be able to request an Independent Medical Review (IMR) from your state's Insurance Department or Managed Care Department. The case is reviewed by experts in the field who are not affiliated with the client's health care plan. <u>You can use this process even if you are an out-of-network provider.</u> And the great news is that IMRs often overrule health plan determinations. For example, in California in 2019, approximately 60% of appeals resulted in the consumer receiving the requested service from the health plan.[39] You may be able to request an expedited review of the grievance for cases that involve an imminent and serious threat to the health of the client if treatment is disrupted. In extreme cases, it may be wise to file grievances with the plan and the state agency at the same time.

You may also be pleased to learn that on several occasions I have had the experience when I have filed a complaint with the state, that the health plan has suddenly reversed its decision or sent a payment, clearly in response to receiving notification from the state of my complaint. Then I will get a letter from the state saying basically "we have talked to the health plan and they are reporting that this issue has been resolved." It seems apparent that the plans want to avoid dealing with a formal complaint, and perhaps it is in their interest to keep their complaint statistics low.

▶ **The client may get the employer's benefits manager involved,** asking them to contact the plan on the client's behalf. This can be highly effective. Only a client should initiate contact with a benefits manager. Once when I was not getting paid by an insurance plan, I asked my client to contact the benefits manager at his company, who was able to get the plan to pay me. Because the employer pays the premiums, and the benefits manager represents the employer, s/he often has more clout at the plan, and can be an influential ally for you. While cost containment is important to healthcare organizations, employer satisfaction is vital to their survival. They know that if enough clients complain about their health plan to their employer, the employer may find a new plan.

▶ **You or your client may have the right to bring a civil case** if a final appeal is denied. Consulting an attorney may be advised.

▶ **If the service will not be covered,** the client may choose to pay you out of pocket. It is wise to have the client sign and return a Private Pay Agreement (see sample on Page 149), stating that the client understands that he or she is obligated to pay for the services to be rendered, that reimbursement was denied by the plan, and the fee. This agreement should be given to the client in advance of providing the out-of-pocket services.

Specific Appeal Situations

1. **If you are not being covered because you are not an HMO or EPO network provider,** you or the client may call or write a letter to the health plan (perhaps with supporting documents from you and/or his doctor) that states the reasons he went to an out-of-network provider, and the reasons it is believed you are the best provider to see. Insurance may pay for out-of-network services when a case can be made that you have qualifications that network providers within a reasonable proximity don't

possess (see "Single Case Agreements," Page 25). They may even pay your full fee, if you negotiate well. However, the plan may not cover past sessions.

2. **If you are a network provider, but the service you provided (or intend to provide) is not a covered service,** be prepared to defend why the plan should make an exception in this case. Focus on cost-efficiency and most effective symptom-reduction. Provide evidence and research, if possible, about your treatment efficacy. See Chapter 9 for ideas.

3. **If they say your license is not covered,** contact your professional organization, and appeal. The Affordable Care Act has made it so that most plans cannot discriminate with respect to participation ... or coverage against any health care provider who is acting within the scope of that provider's license or certification under applicable State law."[40] Also, many states have "Freedom of Choice" laws that mandate that insurance plans may not prohibit their members from selecting certain types of licensed professionals, even if the insurance coverage is provided by an out-of-state plan. However, there are exceptions.

4. **If you are told couples counseling is not covered,** see "Care Denials," Page 43.

5. **If the insurance company told you when you first called that the client was eligible, or covered at a certain rate, or that the deductible would be waived, but the claim said something else:** Jack's employer may not have informed the plan about a change in Jack's employment status or coverage. Or the plan hasn't updated their info. Or the representative you spoke with originally gave you incorrect information. Or Jack may not have paid his premium. Jack may have to pay for your services that the plan denied, but not always.

On occasion, I have persuaded a plan to pay when I was given incorrect coverage information in the initial call to check coverage. One time, I had been told the client was eligible when her plan had terminated. On another client, I had been told her deductible was waived when it wasn't. I had good notes from those calls, including names, when I called, what was said, and call confirmation numbers. I argued that treatment decisions were based on that information in good faith. The claims supervisor in these cases viewed the call notes and listened to the call recording, enabling her to see it had been the representative's mistake, and in both cases I got paid for services. Of course, you can't count on this, as most health plans give a disclaimer on the phone that says that quoted benefits are not guaranteed, and coverage cannot be determined until you submit a claim. But it can be worth a call.

6. **If your claim was denied because you didn't have a necessary authorization in place on the date of service,** call the plan – you may need to talk to a case manager. Sometimes you can get them to retro-authorize (back-date) a treatment authorization for that date of service. Then resubmit the claim with a note attached, including the new authorization number. Remember, you can't bill the client for a denied session if it was due to your error.

Sample Appeal Letter

Barbara Griswold, LMFT
4010 Moorpark Ave. #118
San Jose, California 95117
408.985.0846 BarbGris@aol.com

June 28, 2020

To: CureQuick Insurance, Grievance Coordinator
P.O. Box 248
Summit, N.J. 97901

Re: Client Jack Klutz
CureQuick ID #: NPG5679020
Client DOB: 03/09/58
CPT Code: 90837
Dates of Service: 3/1/2020, 3/8/2020,
　　　　　　　　3/15/2020, 3/22/2020
Claim#: 98765432-00
Total Amount Charged: $510.00

To Whom It May Concern:

I am writing as part of a claim dispute, to ask for reconsideration of your denial of payment for 4 psychotherapy sessions 3/1/20 through 3/22/20 with my client, Jack Klutz.

I initially submitted this claim online via OfficeAlly.com on 4/2/20. When I had not received payment by 5/15/20 I contacted CureQuick Claims Department (800-555-1234) and spoke to Marianne C. (call confirmation #C00691936264086). She said she saw no record of the claim and suggested I mail it to claims address 123 Lost Lane, Paper Trail, MN 55344. I sent it in on 5/20/20. When I still had not received payment by 6/20/2020, I called CureQuick again at the same number (call confirmation #C00691936264333) and spoke to Steve C., a Claims Dept. supervisor. He said the claims address I had been given was incorrect for this member, and that the claim still had not been received. He said I should fax the claim and proof of online filing to him at 1-888-555-3333. On 6/24/20, I printed out proof of filing from Office Ally and faxed it with a copy of the claim.

On 6/24/2020 I received the Explanation of Benefits, and all dates of service had been denied due to late filing (Claim #98765432-00). I called CureQuick on 6/25/20 (1-800-555-1234, call confirmation #C00691936264333) and spoke to claims representative Max G. He said I'd have to file an appeal to have the claim reconsidered.

I not only provided proof of timely filing (copy enclosed), but have made multiple attempts to file in a timely manner. I feel CureQuick should take responsibility for the fact that the claim was delayed in part due to misinformation given by CureQuick staff. In addition, I have provided medically necessary treatment for the member.

Please contact me if you need more information to reconsider this claim.
Sincerely,
Barbara Griswold, LMFT
Licensed Marriage and Family Therapist MFC27210
NPI XXXXXXXX Tax ID #XXXXXXXXX

Questions and Answers

The plan paid for a period of time, then stopped paying (or is demanding reimbursement for paid claims or alleged overpayments). What do I do?

Call the plan to see if you can find out what is going on. You may need to write a formal appeal letter, but call first. You may want to use a legal argument known as estoppel. Since the plan has paid for a period of time, and since the insurance company was responsible for determining the terms and conditions of the contract at the time they initially paid, you might argue that by their reimbursement you had every reason to believe they would continue to pay, and at the same rate, and that you and your client relied on their behavior to make treatment decisions. Thus, it could be argued that the company should be estopped, or barred, from discontinuing treatment (or asking for repayment) once it has made such a "ruling" on the coverage.[41] While there are many types of estoppel, the legal doctrine of promissory estoppel could be used, as it "prevents one party from withdrawing a promise made to a second party if the latter has reasonably relied on that promise."[42] In an example where the plan pays you sessions and later asks for repayment or states it overpaid you, you could use estoppel to argue that:

1. The health plan had all the information it needed to make the correct calculation of benefits in the first place,
2. You had no reason to know that you had been paid the wrong amount,
3. Their payments were reasonably relied upon by you (i.e. you made treatment decisions based on this pattern, since you had no way to know that the plan would not continue to pay),
4. It would be a hardship to repay the amount (or that justice requires enforcement of the plan's original "promise" of payment at the rate originally paid).

If I'm an out-of-network provider, and I've been paid, is it really my role to assist clients in appeals? Shouldn't it be my client's job to hound their plan for payment?

Many professional associations have ethical standards that require their therapist members to advocate for treatment they believe will benefit clients. Assisting a client with an appeal may even be required by state law.

What if the insurance plan wants to see copies of my case notes for the appeal?

If your client signed your standard release form (or the one on the CMS-1500), he has already agreed to allow the release of "any medical information or other information necessary" to process the claims so you can be reimbursed or so you can request treatment approvals. However, it is a good idea to get the client's permission to file an appeal on his behalf. You should explain the appeal process to him, and you may want to have him sign a specific release if you need to submit progress notes as part of an appeal. If your client is hesitant to have his insurance company see these notes, you may suggest he call the insurance company to discuss his concerns about the confidential handling of his health information. Of course, your client always retains the option of paying out-of-pocket for the disputed sessions instead of undergoing a case review.

I want to appeal, but I didn't take good notes while treating this client. Can I write or rewrite my notes before submitting them?

No. I know this is tempting, but rewriting treatment notes may be insurance fraud. You could ask the plan if they will accept a treatment summary, but be sure you give the date that the summary was written, so you don't give the false impression that the summary was written in the past. (Do you shiver when you think about an insurance plan or licensing board looking at your notes? Check out the section of the book on notes on Page 54, and my Progress Notes Webinar, see Resources, Page 133).

Will insurance continue to authorize sessions for my client while I'm appealing a decision?

This depends on the plan, and on the reason you were denied. When it is a clear-cut coverage issue (ex. "we don't cover that service" or "the client hasn't paid their premium"), they probably won't cover it. Or if they are waiting for documentation from you, they may not pay until they get it. However, in most other situations, plans will typically allow you to continue to see the client and reimburse you while you go through the appeal process when there is a dispute over medical necessity (and sometimes if you are asking for an exception to plan rules). This is not always the case, so always call and ask. For a crisis case, seek an expedited review with the health plan, so that the outcome can be determined in a matter of days. If needed, contact your state Department of Insurance for advice (see state DOI contact information in Appendix A on Page 129). Be sure that the client is aware of any financial risks involved with continuing in therapy.

The insurance company is requesting that I repay an overpayment, and I am contesting it. Can I delay repayment while I appeal?

Usually, yes, but be sure to ask the insurance plan for its policy. In cases where repayment is requested, call the plan's overpayment department (or the financial recovery service, if you've been contacted by one), ask for an extension, and ask them to document that you are filing an appeal, so you don't get any (more) threatening letters when they don't receive payment. Also, you don't want them to begin trying to collect by withholding future payments on this or other cases. This sometimes happens when you don't repay CureQuick for one client -- they eventually deduct the amount they say you owe from your payments for other members until the "debt" is paid off. For this reason, try to get something in writing verifying that they have given you an extension.

14

Electronic Billing
With or Without a Computer
ℬ ℭ

The pressure to bill electronically is stronger than ever, as plans seek to lower costs by encouraging providers to do all their transactions online. However, it appears that psychotherapists may be slower to embrace online filing than their medical colleagues. While one survey showed only 6% of healthcare providers file paper claims, a survey of psychotherapists showed that almost 30% of them were still mailing or faxing paper claims.[43, 44]

But paper claims may become obsolete, as some plans only accept electronic claims. In fact, many health plans are requiring new providers to have internet access, and to submit claims electronically. Plan that still accept paper claims may no longer accept handwritten ones, requiring that they be filled out with a computer program.

And as more therapists went online in 2020 to provide telehealth sessions in response to the COVID-19 pandemic shelter-in-place orders, electronic billing also saw a rise in popularity.

What's to gain? The computer gives us 24-hour access to many insurance plans. In addition to electronic billing, plan websites may enable you to:

- ▶ Check benefits and eligibility
- ▶ Submit claims, and check claim status
- ▶ Check authorization status, number of sessions authorized, and expirations
- ▶ Download forms and applications, and submit requests for more sessions
- ▶ Update your practice information and availability to see new clients
- ▶ View lists of network providers (to assist with referrals)
- ▶ Create a personal statement and practice profile, which prospective clients can view
- ▶ Access medical necessity guidelines, appeal procedures, etc.
- ▶ Correspond with insurance company staff and ask questions

Types of Electronic Billing

Electronic billing is the submission of claims to the insurance plan via the Internet. But there are multiple ways to do this. You don't even need a computer -- you only need to hire someone who has one! Here are the four most common types of electronic billing:

1. **Submit directly at the plan's website.** When an insurance plan has the capacity to accept claims through their website, no special software is required on your end. You go to the plan website, log in with your provider ID and password (or follow the directions if you're a first time user -- you may have to call the plan to get an ID and password), then log in and follow the instructions to file claims. It's free and easy, even for the computer novice. It's usually fairly quick since the plan has the member's information already pre-populated on the forms -- you don't have to enter it each time. You just add the diagnosis and session information, such as dates, CPT codes, and fees.

   Claims are filed directly and immediately with the insurance company, and you can print out immediate proof of filing, with a confirmation number. The confidential information is encrypted so it is secure. Always print a copy of claims you submit online (or at least your claims submission confirmation page) to keep in the client's chart, and keep a record of what claims were filed when.

   This is a good option for therapists who don't have a large number of claims to file or who work with a limited number of insurance companies.

2. **Submit through your billing program and a clearinghouse.** This is a popular option for therapists who have (or are willing to get) a billing or practice management program. The program may be an online subscription program (such as SimplePractice, TherapyNotes, or Theranest) or a software program that lives in your computer. The claims are transmitted from your program to a clearinghouse with whom you have contracted. A clearinghouse is a service that serves as a go-between between your practice program and the insurance plans. The clearinghouse instantaneously converts the claims from your practice management program to a secure format, then transmits them electronically to each plan. So rather than sending a separate claim to each health insurer as a separate transaction, the clearinghouse serves as a central portal to transmit claims to multiple plans. You (or your practice management program) send your claims to the clearinghouse, and the clearinghouse then forwards the claims to the appropriate health insurer. Like giving your mail to the post office, they deliver it for you – but instantaneously!

   I use the clearinghouse Office Ally (www.OfficeAlly.com) with my practice software. They have an extensive list of plans they can bill. Best of all, the clearinghouse catches many errors before the claim is sent, and e-mails me with the status of submitted claims, keeping a record of my submissions that I can use for proof of filing. And their customer service folks will walk even the most timid through the process. Office Ally can even be used by out-of-network therapists to submit bills on their client's behalf.

   Submitting via a clearinghouse may be an option to consider if you work with many insurance clients and/or multiple insurance companies, and if you have (or are willing to get) a billing or practice management program. Contact the clearinghouse to make sure the plans you bill for are on the list of those payers they bill electronically, and that they can receive claims from your billing program. And before you purchase a billing program, ask about the clearinghouse it uses, and make sure it can bill for the insurance plans you bill (for billing programs and Office Ally contact info, *see* Resources, Page 133).

3. **Submit through a claims clearinghouse <u>without</u> your own billing program.** Don't have your own billing software? OfficeAlly.com also has free online practice management software you can use called Practice Mate, which allows you to create and maintain a patient database, with client demographics, insurance information, and visit information, as well as to create superbills and print or electronically submit claims.

    Again, this may be an option to consider if you work with many insurance clients and/or multiple insurance companies, or can't submit at the insurance plan's website. It is a good idea to contact the clearinghouse to make sure the insurance plans you plan to bill are on their payer list.

4. **Submit through a billing service.** Here's an option for those of you who don't want to deal with computers or billing: Hire a billing service. A billing service is a good choice even if you have practice billing software but don't want to deal with claims submission and follow-up. After you fax, mail, or e-mail your client data to the billing service (you'll need to provide some log of clients seen, date seen, and procedure codes), the service will format and transmit the claims, and bill the appropriate insurance company, via website, mail, or clearinghouse.

    For an additional fee, most billing services offer other services, including follow-up on unpaid claims, dealing with claims problems, verifying insurance coverage for new clients, tracking authorizations, and recredentialing assistance. Financial arrangements vary: Billing services may offer flat-fee pricing (a set amount per month regardless of number of claims filed), per-claim fees, or may charge a certain percentage of reimbursements received from the insurance plan.

    Karen Rose, MFT, loves her billing service. "They do all paperwork for my practice, including billing, tracking claims, dealing with unpaid claims, credentialing and re-credentialing. In fact, I now print on the back of my business cards, 'for billing questions, contact...' with their phone number. This way, my clients contact them directly regarding billing and insurance issues, and I can just do therapy. Maybe I do one extra hour of therapy per month to pay for the service, but it is totally worth it."[45] Sounds nice, huh? (If interested in my Billing Service List, including a list of over 30 billers and their services and fees, reviews from therapists who use them, and suggested interview questions to ask when hiring a biller, *see* Resources, Page 133).

Electronic Billing: What's in It for Therapists?

▶ **Faster payment.** The biggest payoff is that directly-filed electronic claims are instantaneously received by the insurance company, which greatly speeds payment. In addition, electronic claims are typically given priority processing status over paper claims.

▶ **Less delay and denials due to errors.** Electronic billing has built-in alerts that call your attention to errors, flagging missing or invalid information before you file or soon afterwards. If there is a problem with the claim, such as a missing or invalid CPT code or diagnosis code, it may be identified before the program allows you to submit the claim so you can correct it. You don't have to wait six weeks to find out when the claim is denied. Other errors, such as incorrect policyholder ID numbers or claims addresses, may be identified within a few days, so that you can submit a corrected claim. This quick identification of problems dramatically decreases the likelihood that your claim will be denied, which means faster payment and fewer hassles for you.

▶ **More security.** While you may be concerned about confidentiality of information submitted electronically, some plans argue there is more security in electronic transmission than "snail mail." Electronic claims are encrypted (translated into a coded message), so they are secure and in compliance with HIPAA security standards.

▶ **Cost savings.** If you choose to file claims directly on the company's website or via a clearinghouse, you save the cost of claim forms, envelopes, and postage. A CAQH study showed that submitting electronically meant a savings of almost 75 percent.[46] And even a billing service might save you money, once you figure in the cost of the time you would have spent doing all that they will do, and income lost from denied claims or those you neglected to file in a timely manner or follow up with.

▶ **It's simple.** If you can fill out a CMS-1500 form by hand, you can do it online.

▶ **Reducing paper in your office, and saving trees.** Filing claims online, signing up to allow the plan to e-mail you with newsletters or announcements, and direct deposit of your claims payment check can all save paper.

▶ **Easy tracking of claims.** You are typically given proof of online filing, so that you can prove you filed in a timely manner if the health plan ever questions this. You can always check the status of claims you've submitted, preventing "lost" claims. However, it is still important to follow up if you are not paid on time. I once contacted a plan when I hadn't been paid, and was told they hadn't received the claim from my clearinghouse. When I resubmitted the claim, it was denied for "lack of timely filing," and my appeal was denied, despite proof I provided of timely electronic filing. While with most plans this proof would be all that would be needed to overturn this denial, in this case the plan said that they could not be held accountable for clearinghouse problems. I appealed to my State Department of Managed Care and won. I learned from this to have a system in place that would alert me to unpaid claims before too much time passes.

Questions and Answers

If I do electronic billing, do I have to deal with HIPAA regulations?

You bet. If you do any type of electronic billing using the internet, *or if someone does it on your behalf* (a billing service, a claims clearinghouse, an employee or independent contractor, etc.), or exchanges a client's information with insurance plans via e-mail, you automatically become a "covered entity" under HIPAA regulations. Once you are a covered entity, you will need to obtain a National Provider Identifier (NPI) to use on claims/invoices, and must give a Notice of Privacy Policies to ALL your clients. In addition, other HIPAA policies and procedures must be followed, both with your private pay and insurance clients. For more information on HIPAA, see the HIPAA section of this manual (Page 33), or the HIPAA/NPI Information section of Resources (Page 133).

Is buying a billing or practice management software a good idea for me?

This depends on the size of your insurance practice. Obviously, if you have only a few insurance clients, you might just fill out all claims by hand for now. However, as we said earlier, handwritten claims are more likely to be denied due to legibility issues, take longer to process, and the plan may stop accepting them. You may decide to go to the website of each client's insurance and submit claims there, if available, since these will be processed more quickly. However, if you have a large number of insurance clients, a billing program can be a real time-saver. Even if you do file by mail, with one click many billing programs can take the client data you've entered into the program and print out the data into blank CMS-1500 forms for a whole month's worth of sessions. And, since computer-printed claim forms are typically processed more quickly by the plan, you may want to look into Office Ally's Practice Mate, their practice management program, or something similar.

If you were thinking about buying your own billing or practice management program, In my last survey of 500 therapists, SimplePractice was the most popular, and is very highly rated by its users. It includes integrated Wiley Treatment Plans and lots of customizable options. But do shop around. In the Resources section (starting Page 133), I've given the contact information for Capterra, which has an online referral list of mental health billing software and reviews of many of these programs, giving links to their websites. Many billing software programs will give you a free demo period, so you can "test-drive" different packages before purchase. If you are like me and your handwriting is so illegible you can't even read your own grocery lists, you may want to choose a program that allows you to type session notes. More deluxe programs may include progress notes, authorization tracking, referral and cash flow statistics, medication trackers, sample treatment plans, reports, sample letters, practice expense logs, client scheduling, and the ability to export financial information to Quicken or QuickBooks. Remember that not all practice management programs offer the ability to bill electronically, and others charge extra for this feature.

Do all insurance plans accept electronic claims at their website?

No, but most large ones do. For those that don't, they may offer an affiliated electronic portal such as Availity, or you can bill by mail, have your clearinghouse bill by mail, or you can hire a billing service to bill those plans for you.

So, can I get _paid_ electronically, too?

Yes, from many plans, and this is the wave of the future. The push is on for the "paperless office," and some plans, including Aetna, Blue Cross, Blue Shield, and United Health Care, are now able to pay providers electronically through an Electronic Funds Transfer (EFT) right into your bank account.   While each plan is a bit different, typically once a provider signs up for a plan's Electronic Payment Service, claim payments are directly deposited. An e-mail notification is sometimes sent to the therapist when a claim is processed, and EOBs may be viewed and downloaded by going onto the plan's website (or the EOB may continue to come in the mail). Electronic payment is available whether you submit claims electronically or by mail. Some health plans are insisting that providers sign up for electronic funds transfers. One plan said they would only make exceptions for low-volume providers, those who share a Tax ID number, or for clinicians who don't have Internet access or a bank account.

I don't like electronic payment because even though you may get an e-mail alerting you to a payment, I have to go to my bank website to be sure I received the payment, and may have to go to the plan website to view the EOB and print it out, then must match this payment to the clients and dates of service I was paid for. When you have a lot of insurance clients and work with a lot of different plans, this can take more time than processing paper checks and paper EOBs.

Any recommendations when it comes to choosing a billing program?

First, consider carefully what you need your program to do. You may feel you only need a program that prints out a CMS-1500 form for billing. But I am so happy I went with a more robust program so I could record client notes, medications, and prepare invoices in addition to claims for electronic billing. More deluxe programs Like SimplePractice even integrated treatment planning software in the program and customizable note templates, and a way to keep track of payments received from clients and insurance plans. Also look at what kind of customer support is offered.

The folks at TameYourPractice.com (see Page 135) can interview you about your needs and help you choose a billing program or electronic health record (EHR) program that is right for you.

Any recommendations when it comes to choosing a billing service?

Get referrals from other mental health professionals who have a billing service. I recommend you find a service that specializes in mental health billing, which can be quite different than medical billing. They should have lots of experience working with plans in your state -- insurance plans operate so differently in each state, and that experience with plan expectations can make all the difference. Shop around, getting estimates from different services. Write out and sign clear agreements about all expectations and fees. Interview billers, and call their references. Remember that you don't necessarily need to find someone who has an office close to you; it is possible that all communication may take place via phone, fax, or e-mail. Most importantly, monitor them closely – ask for regular reports outlining which plans have been billed for what clients and what dates of services, so if something happens with the billing service you could pick up where they left off at any time (see also my Billing Service List, Resources, Page 133).

15

Clinical Issues & Confidentiality

ಐ ೞ

So, as Jack's therapy progresses, how will taking his insurance affect his treatment?

Clinical Issues

▶ **You may need to spend some session time discussing coverage.** You may need to educate Jack about network vs. out-of-network provider options, copayments, deductibles, limitations of coverage, and pre-authorization. Jack may think he has coverage for unlimited yearly visits, but may not know that these sessions will be given to him only if his plan determines that they are medically necessary. He may walk in ready to pay his copay, not realizing he may have a substantial deductible to use up before his insurance pays a dime.

▶ **Brief goal emphasis.** Perhaps the most significant way that managed care has changed therapy is the emphasis on short-term, cognitive-behavioral, evidence-based, symptom-focused therapies. Of course, you can do any type of treatment that you and the client decide is best. But if your client wants his insurance to cover the sessions, it's important to remember that insurance is illness-based, and may only pay for treatment aimed at symptom-reduction instead of the in-depth exploration of personal growth, life goals, career counseling, communication skills, or even childhood issues if unrelated to a current symptom. And it isn't just that the insurance plans are coming to expect counseling to be briefer and more goal-directed – this has affected the expectations of some clients.

▶ **Clients may stop coming when benefits end.** Instead of continuing and paying out of pocket when he runs out of sessions, Jack may be tempted to take a break and only restart counseling when his benefits renew or after his deductible is used up elsewhere. It can be a challenge to help clients to make treatment decisions that are not based solely on benefits.

▶ **Clients may be unable to see the therapist of their choice if the therapist is not covered by insurance.** If Jack changes to a health plan where you are not a participating provider, or if you leave the CureQuick provider panel, he may not be able to afford to continue with you, and might need to find a new therapist. In many cases, this can also mean that Jack is unable to see the professional best suited to meet his needs, or a specialist you would like him to see (i.e. a psychiatrist with an expertise in treating pail phobias), if the specialist is not a network provider (for exceptions, see Page 25 for Single Case Agreements and Transition of Care Agreements).

▶ **Think outside the box.** While once-a-week therapy is often the norm, if Jack only has limited sessions or has a high deductible, he may want to space sessions out.

▶ **Insurance plans will expect you to create a treatment plan for every client at the beginning of treatment.** Treatment plans should include your treatment goals, objectives (how you will measure these goals have been achieved), your intended treatment modality and interventions, and dates you feel each goal can reasonably be achieved. Goals and objectives should be specific, measurable, realistic, and focused on symptom-reduction. As you go through treatment, you can add new goals that come up along the way. It is a good idea to review the treatment plan periodically throughout treatment with the client, noting progress, and checking off goals, as appropriate. (For more on Treatment Plans, see my webinar on Progress Notes and Treatment Plans -- see Resources, Page 133).

▶ **Set goals that take into account session limitations.** If the client has only a few sessions, and does not have the ability to continue with you after these benefits run out, set realistic goals that can be achieved within the given time frame. You may choose to become more focused in your work, and ask the client to choose one specific issue to focus on.

▶ **Monitor your negative counter-transference.** It is easy to get resentful about the plan's fee discounts, limitations, and paperwork, and take it out on your insurance clients. You may find yourself giving preferential treatment to full-fee, private pay clients, like calling them back first, or giving them the best time slots. Or you may feel annoyed when your (discount fee) insurance client discusses his recent luxury car purchase or yachting adventures. Take responsibility for your choices, and don't take insurance frustrations out on your clients. You wouldn't want your own medical providers to hold it against you because you used your insurance. Also, don't speak negatively about the plan to the client. If this gets back to the plan, you may get a phone call from them.

▶ **High-risk and substance abuse cases may mean more contact with case managers.** It is wise to share any serious concerns about risk issues (suicide attempts, suicide risk, violence, substance abuse, homicide, child abuse) with a case manager at the plan. This helps protect you in the event that Jack destabilizes, harms himself, or harms someone else. Case managers can also be helpful in suggesting resources the plan may provide or cover. For example, if you found Jack had become dependent on alcohol, you might contact CureQuick to discuss treatment options covered by the plan before presenting them to Jack.

▶ **If you'd like to see Jack more than one hour daily, and you want insurance to cover it, you would usually need permission from the plan.** Most plans will only reimburse for one hour of outpatient therapy per day, unless prior approval is given. As always, ask the insurance company.

▶ **If Jack can't afford his copayment, co-insurance or deductible**, you may be tempted to help him out by waiving it. Read more about why you shouldn't on Page 101.

Confidentiality Issues

When discussing the topic of insurance, perhaps one of the biggest concerns of therapists and clients is confidentiality. Despite state laws and HIPAA protections, clients who use their insurance are concerned about how their private health information will be used, and with whom it may be shared. This is especially understandable since the sensitive topics discussed in therapy (such as a client's sexual orientation, HIV status, infidelity, or abuse of drugs or alcohol) could have devastating consequences if disclosed to the wrong parties.

In one survey 67 percent of respondents were concerned about the privacy of their medical records, and 52 percent were concerned that claim information might be used by an employer to limit job opportunities.[47] In fact, 13 percent said they had done something to protect the privacy of their medical history. These protective behaviors included paying out of pocket to avoid submitting an insurance claim, not seeking care to avoid disclosure, avoiding a visit to the doctor for treatment of certain conditions, asking a provider not to write down a health condition, giving inaccurate or incomplete information on a medical form, requesting care under an assumed name, or asking a therapist not to take notes. The survey also found that clients were largely unaware of their privacy rights.

Yet despite these concerns, survey respondents reported a favorable view of new health technology which allows treating providers to store and share medical records, with a majority (59%) willing to share personal health information when it could result in better medical treatment.

What do I say when Jack asks, "how much of what I say here can get back to my employer?"

One response would be to say, "What is your concern?" so you can be sure to target the client's fears. You might tell the client that "what you say in our session, and even your presence, is confidential. It is my ethical and legal duty which I take very seriously. Even if your wife or boss called and asked if you were here, I couldn't confirm or deny it without your written consent. Your insurance company is also obliged by law to protect your confidentiality. No information is released by me or by your plan to your employer, unless you are a mandatory management referral, where there may be some limited communication. In EAP cases, the health plan may report some statistical information to the employer (for example, how many EAP visits were used overall by employees), but data is not client-specific, so your name or identifying information would not be used." You could then review exceptions to confidentiality, which should also be in your treatment agreement (see Sample Treatment Agreement, Page 143). If Jack is still concerned about confidentiality issues, you might outline the security measures you take to protect his private information, physical files, computer notes, and computer files or electronic billing. You might also recommend that he contact his insurance company to discuss the plan's confidentiality policies. Of course, he may always choose to pay out of pocket instead.

Should Jack be concerned that using his insurance might be troublesome for him later if he applies for future health or life insurance policies?

Clients are often concerned if they use insurance that this could in some way come back to haunt them. They might be particularly concerned that it might affect their ability to get a future health or insurance policy. Because you have to give a diagnosis on a claim form that is submitted to the health plan, Jack might be concerned that such a "paper trail" of his treatment and mental health condition could become a problem for him later on -- for example, if he lost his employer-sponsored group health coverage and needs to apply for an individual health plan. Unlike group plans, where applicants are not asked medical history questions, individual health or life insurance plan applicants in the past have had to go through medical scrutiny.

In the past, if Jack was honest about his health conditions (including mental health conditions), the plan might have denied Jack coverage altogether, or excluded coverage for the "pre-existing health condition" for which you treated him, or charged a premium significantly higher than normal since he is considered at a higher risk for illness.

But things have changed a bit in this arena. The Affordable Care Act now prohibits these discriminatory health care plan practices, both for children and adults. Health plans covered by the ACA -- which includes many that are offered by the federal or state government marketplaces, and even most plans offered direct from health plans -- can't ask about pre-existing health conditions when setting premiums. They must charge the same for those with

health conditions as for the healthy, and can't refuse to cover a client because of a health condition (for more on the ACA, see Page 36).

Unfortunately, the ACA does not apply to life insurance plans, so life insurance plans are still able to discriminate based on pre-existing health conditions. Also, a diagnosis and "paper trail" could also become an issue if Jack is pursuing Top Secret clearance or applying for other special government clearances.

If Jack still isn't sure whether to use his insurance, here is something to keep in mind: On the individual life insurance plan application or top-secret clearance application, Jack may be asked if he has seen a therapist or doctor within a certain period of time prior to the application, and what provider he saw. He would then be asked to sign a release so that Jack's therapist could be contacted about the presenting issues, diagnosis, course and length of treatment. <u>So, the outcome may be the same whether Jack uses his insurance to pay for your sessions or pays out of pocket</u> – Jack's confidentiality is not protected by paying out of pocket.

Should I make Jack aware of the type of information I have to send to his insurance? Should I tell him that the plan has the right to look at his progress notes?

You may want to inform all your insurance clients about the types of information you'll need to send to an insurance plan. You could write a few lines in your treatment agreement specifically identifying the kind of information you may be asked to release (see Sample Treatment Agreement, Page 143). Or you could do it on a case-by-case basis, only informing clients who express confidentiality concerns. You could show Jack blank copies of any treatment request or claim forms you may need to submit to his plan, and explain the type of information required to process claims or request authorizations.

"I can't stress enough that whenever you bill an insurance company for something, they have the right to see your notes -- even if you're not a contracted provider," says Susan Frager, owner of Psych Admin Partners, a mental health billing service.[48] So you might also explain that if Jack chooses to use insurance, he is agreeing to allow the health plan to view your case notes, if needed, to approve further treatment, evaluate for medical necessity, or ensure the quality of your care. Then Jack can make an informed choice whether to use his insurance. While you could stress that insurance plans are also obligated to protect his confidentiality, he might want to contact his plan to find out more about how it handles confidential data. If he doesn't feel comfortable after this exchange, he can choose to pay out-of-pocket.

What if it becomes clear that I will need to disclose sensitive information in Jack's case in order to get more sessions approved?

While the client may have signed a release allowing you to disclose "any information necessary" to obtain insurance reimbursement, a therapist should make every effort to protect a client's confidential private health information. Don't reveal any more information than you must in order to get treatment authorized or a claim processed -- using or disclosing more than the minimum necessary protected health information can be a HIPAA violation (see Page 35). But sometimes it will be necessary to reveal sensitive information in order to receive reimbursement or get authorization for continued treatment. In these cases, it may be wise to talk with Jack about the information that will need to be revealed so he can make an informed choice about whether to allow the release. Again, he may decide he would rather not use his insurance to pay for your sessions if this type of exchange of information is necessary. Be sure to document your conversation and your client's decision, and have him sign a Private-Pay Agreement if he decides to waive his right to use his insurance (see Sample Private-Pay Agreement, Page 149).

I have a client who is seeking therapy, using her husband's insurance plan, but she doesn't want her husband to know she is in treatment. Can he find out?

Whenever a plan member (in this case, the wife) uses benefits, the primary subscriber (here, the husband) normally receives a copy of treatment authorizations and claims payments. These might even be addressed to him, and would arrive by mail (or e-mail) at the address the plan has on record. While these may have only basic information on them, it could alert your client's husband that she is receiving treatment, the treating provider's name and address, and what type of treatment is being received. This is a fact most clients are not aware of, which could be a significant factor in their decision to use their insurance, especially in certain cases. I advise telling clients up front if you suspect this might be an issue of concern, especially in cases of domestic violence or other situations where the client feels unsafe. Your client might want to call her insurance plan to see if arrangements can be made to create a secure therapy environment for her.

Are there any special precautions I have to take for insurance records?

Most insurance companies and HIPAA require client records to be kept in a secure manner (for example, locked files and/or password-protected computer files). You should have policies and procedures for protecting the confidentiality of any stored or electronically-transmitted client information, and for purging of records in a manner that protects confidentiality. If you are a HIPAA covered entity (see Chapter 7 for more on this), and even if you aren't, you will want to follow the guidelines outlined in HIPAA for the security of all client records. I recommend you take a HIPAA class or webinar, or read a book on the topic. (Also see Page 116 for more on records requests, and advice on how to respond).

16

14 Ways to Jeopardize Your License: Common Types of Insurance Fraud

༄ ❧

Most of us become therapists because we want to help people, not because we are financial wizards. In all our years of coursework, we may never have taken a class in running a small business, or in dealing with insurance plans. Because we may not be well-informed about the financial aspects of our practices, we can end up making decisions that we don't even know are illegal or unethical.

In some cases, our resentment about contract restrictions and discounts may cause us to be less than completely honest in our billing. You may feel these big insurance plans can afford it, and no one will find out. In other cases, you may bend the truth in a well-intentioned attempt to assist clients, to help them afford therapy. Some of these practices have become so common that many therapists even forget that what they are really doing is misrepresenting their services to health plans solely for the purpose of getting reimbursed.

So how exactly do we know we've left the land of trying to help clients, and entered the territory of insurance fraud? Michael Brandt, a fraud investigator for HealthNet Insurance, writes that "health care fraud is deception or misrepresentation by providers, employers, members, or any person acting on their behalf with knowledge that the deception could result in some unauthorized payment or benefit."[48] Note that this definition includes people "acting on your behalf," such as billing services or clearinghouses you have hired. Fraud is typically afoot whenever you alter billing facts for sessions in order to increase likelihood of reimbursement.

Here's a quick rundown of some common fraud traps that are easy to fall into:

1. **Choosing or changing a diagnosis to increase the likelihood of payment.** I am often asked, "what diagnosis should I put on the claim so I'll be paid?" My answer is, of course, "put down whatever is true, without regard for reimbursement." Otherwise, you are misrepresenting the diagnosis. Diagnosis-related fraud includes:

   ▶ **Giving a diagnosis when none exists.** It is fraud to submit a claim giving a diagnosis of a mental illness when one does not exist. This may be especially tempting if a client or couple seeks counseling for issues related to self-esteem, communication, career issues, or personal growth, but there is no diagnosable mental illness present (as classified in the DSM). If you do choose a diagnosis, be confident you could defend it later to an insurance company, or in court, if it came to that. Document the symptoms that support your diagnosis in your case notes. Remember that a phase-of-life issue (Z-code) alone typically will not be covered, except by EAPs.

   ▶ **Changing Diagnosis:** It is sometimes tempting to give the client a more serious diagnosis than they actually have in the hopes that this will give them better or longer coverage. For example, you may feel if you upgrade Jack's diagnosis from Adjustment Disorder to Major Depression, Jack might be given additional sessions. Jack may even ask you to do this. But this is fraud if he does not meet the diagnostic criteria. While you may always add a diagnosis, a diagnosis should not be changed unless a mistake was made in the original diagnosis, additional information has led you to another diagnosis, or the client's condition has changed.

   ▶ **Under-diagnosing:** Jack may ask you not to tell the plan about his alcohol abuse. But it could be considered fraud if you only put down his diagnosis of Adjustment Disorder and not his substance abuse diagnosis. Why? Because the insurance plan might have made different treatment approval or reimbursement decisions if they knew the full diagnostic picture. Also, problems could arise if there are discrepancies between your treatment notes and your billing diagnosis. While I have heard therapists say they give the same "innocuous" diagnosis to all their insurance clients, this is clearly fraud, and you could find yourself in trouble if this pattern was ever noticed, or if your client records were audited.

   To reiterate, never give a diagnosis that you couldn't defend in court, or that would make you lose sleep the night before you had to testify. Log the symptoms of the diagnosis in the client's chart.

2. **Billing insurance for cancelled or missed sessions without making it clear that the appointment was missed.** I do not know of any insurance companies that pay for cancelled sessions or no-shows. Because of this, I don't recommend you bill the plan for a missed appointment. Some EAPs will reimburse for a missed session, so check your contract (if you are a plan provider) or call them. If you are allowed by any EAP to bill for missed sessions, ask what CPT code to use on the bill or claim. Don't use a CPT code that would give the impression that the session took place. On any invoice you give a client, be sure "missed/late-cancelled session" is clearly spelled out in your service description. Remember that some insurance contracts do not allow you to bill the client for missed sessions, but in my experience most plans will allow it when the client has agreed in writing and in advance to pay for missed sessions.

100

3. **Charging the health plan more than your usual fee if you are an out-of-network provider.** It would be fraud, for example, to charge Jack's insurance $200 per session if your usual fee for non-insurance clients is $150 – $200 is a misrepresentation of your actual fee. In your practice, you should have a designated "full fee" that you charge for sessions. This doesn't mean you need to abandon your sliding-fee scale. It is OK to slide <u>down</u> from your usual fee, just not <u>up</u> past your full fee when billing insurance plans. While this is not an issue for network therapists, who have a contracted fee, if you are an out-of-network therapist, it may be tempting to charge insurance companies more per session than your full fee in order to get a higher reimbursement rate for you or your clients.

4. **Waiving client copayments, co-insurance, or deductible in advance.** When billing insurance, network providers may not tell the client in advance that he doesn't need to pay his copayment or deductible. As part of your contract, you agreed to collect copayments, so waiving these is a violation of those contracts. More importantly, if your contracted rate with CureQuick is $85, and you told Jack before the session he didn't need to pay his $20 copayment, you are billing the insurance for $85 with the intention of only collecting $65 for the session, which is fraud.

   Does this mean you can't offer a sliding-scale fee? Not when Jack has a flat copayment, as that is an amount set by the insurance plan. But if Jack has a coinsurance (where he pays a percentage of the contracted rate), you could choose to slide your fee. For example, if Jack has a 40% coinsurance, you could cut your fee from $85 to $50, this would cut his portion of the payment from $34.00 to $20.00 But in this case, you should bill the insurance plan only $50 per session, so that you are being honest about the amount you intend to collect for the session.

   Keep in mind that waiving copayments or coinsurances in advance is not the same as forgiving balances the client has left unpaid. You can forgive a balance as long as you have made reasonable attempts to collect and as long as the debt wasn't waived at the beginning of treatment.

5. **Balance-billing clients if you a network provider.** As was mentioned, network providers are not permitted to bill the client for any amount above their contracted rate for a session. If your full fee is $150 and your contracted rate is $75, you cannot collect the remaining $75 difference from the client.

6. <u>Not</u> **balance-billing the client if you are an out-of-network provider.** If you are an out-of-network provider and you have not been paid in full by the client, and you are billing on the client's behalf, you <u>must</u> collect the difference between the session fee stated on the claim form and what the plan paid. Otherwise, if you billed the plan for a $150 session, and were paid $60 by the plan, and did not collect the remaining $90 from the client, the $150 you put on the claim was a fraudulent amount. Once again, you have the option of sliding your fee before filing a claim, but you must report this reduced fee on the claim form. I emphasize, this issue only applies in cases when an out-of-network provider does not accept payment in full by the client at the session. As mentioned earlier, I recommend out-of-network providers do collect payment in full at the session.

7. **Reporting that you provided individual therapy when you saw a couple, or vice versa in order to be paid (or paid more) for the session.** Here's a common one: Let's say you are working with Jack and Jill as a couple, but you aren't sure insurance covers

that service, or you know that Jack's insurance pays more for 60-minute individual sessions (CPT code 90837). So, you use the 90837 code for your couples therapy sessions, even though it is an individual therapy code (as clarified by the AMA in 2017). Or maybe during ongoing couples therapy, you decide to see Jill alone, and bill using a 90847 couples therapy code instead of the more appropriate 90846 (family therapy without patient present), since you believe it pays more. Misrepresenting the CPT code in order to get reimbursed or increase reimbursement is fraud.

8. Providing a couples therapy session, and billing both partners' insurance companies for an individual therapy session. Simply put, this is duplicate billing for a single service. Also, because the CPT codes are different for individual and couples session, this is misrepresenting the service provided. If you bill both plans for couples therapy, you need to bill the primary insurance first, and secondary insurance after the primary has paid, letting each insurance plan know about the other's coverage and payments (for more on double coverage, see Chapter 17).

9. **Having someone else (a licensed or network provider) sign your claims, or having pre-licensed therapists sign in a way that might make them appear licensed.** If you are not licensed, or not a network provider, or your license is not covered under the health plan, you should not have a covered license holder sign for you and make it look like they provided the service. The consequences for misrepresenting the service provider can be severe. Even when an insurance plan does pay for an unlicensed person for a period of time, at a later date they may find out they paid someone they shouldn't have, and request that the money be paid back to them.

Pre-licensed therapists are typically not covered by private health plans, and so interns, associates and trainees should not bill for care without plan approval. If the insurance company does reimburse pre-licensed providers, the treating therapist and supervisor should both sign, identifying themselves on the claim with their roles and titles such as "Joe Jones, AMFT23456, under supervision of Jennifer Smith, MFT87463." No attempt should be made by the agency, group practice, or pre-licensed therapist to hide the identity and licensure status of the treating therapist.

10. **Billing two insurance companies for the same service(s) with the intent to collect your full fee from both of them.** The bottom line? You may not collect more than your full fee for any given session.

11. **Billing for sessions where the client was late.** One example of this would be billing for a 60-minute session even though Jack was 15 minutes late, and you only saw him for 45 minutes. In this case, it would be more ethical to bill the insurance for a 45-minute session. Don't forget, insurance plans often require that session start and stop times be documented in the client notes, so billing for a longer session than was provided may be discovered in an audit of the chart. So now you will ask, "can I

charge the client for the time I waited for them?" Great question. This seems to be an area not typically addressed in plan contracts, and good luck getting a clear answer from a knowledgeable person at the health plan. If you want to charge a client when they are late, this should be clearly outlined in your treatment agreement in advance.

12. **Billing for video or phone sessions as if the client was in office.** If you know video or phone sessions are not covered, you may not bill as if the session took place in person in order to get reimbursed. If you bill make it clear on the bill or claim that it was via video by using the appropriate codes (usually Place of Service code 02 and modifier "95" or "GT" after the CPT code (see Page 69 for more on video or phone sessions).

13. **Rewriting case notes before an insurance case review, audit or appeal.** This is falsifying documents, and you may be guilty of insurance fraud.

14. **Changing service dates.** You may be tempted t on the claim in order to be covered by an authorization that has since expired, or to back-date sessions because a client has since lost coverage. Or if you know the insurance plan won't cover your two-hour session, you might think about submitting a bill for two separate one-hour sessions on different days. However, reporting that you saw a client on a day you didn't is insurance fraud (see more on extended sessions on Page 68).

Perhaps one of the biggest consequences of doing any of these behaviors is that any small irregularity in your billing could come the attention of the insurance plan during a random documentation audit or a claims review. This could lead to a more intensive investigation of all your billing with that company. If billing issues are found, they can ask to recoup large amounts of monies they have paid. I've seen it happen.

"Do not allow yourself to be misled or manipulated by your clients who convincingly ask for your assistance in reducing their financial burdens at the expense of their insurance companies," writes Mary Riemersma, former Executive Director of the California Association of Marriage and Family Therapists. "You are the therapist, the one in control of the situation, and you should be the role model. The costs to you as the therapist can be very great should you be charged with insurance fraud or some other violation of law."[50] In addition, from a clinical perspective, you would be essentially entering into an illicit conspiracy with your client against the insurance company, an agreement which could taint the therapy, and negatively affect the therapist/client relationship.

17

Couples, Families, and "Double Coverage"

ಬ ಆ

When Jack fell down the hill, his wife Jill came tumbling after him – literally and emotionally. Things have been pretty tense at their household since Jack's fall put him out of work, and Jack requests couples therapy instead of individual sessions.

While discussed at different points in this manual, many of the following points bear repeating here, since treating couples brings up challenges when working with insurance.

Couples or Family Therapy

▶ **Will insurance cover it?** Most insurance plans and Employee Assistance Programs cover couples and family therapy, but a few plans don't. If covered, plans typically will cover couples or family therapy only when one covered member in the room has a diagnosable mental disorder that has arisen from family dynamics, or that you are bringing in the family to assist in treatment. Most plans will require more than just a "relational issue" type of diagnosis (a Z-code in the DSM-5). While the clients may have requested couples or family counseling, you are the clinician, and it's your diagnosis that matters. it's a good idea to document why you feel couples or family counseling is a good modality for treating the client's symptoms. But remember: it is insurance fraud to overstate or create a diagnosis for a family member for the purpose of ensuring reimbursement (for more about fraud, see Chapter 16).

▶ **Be sure to use the proper CPT codes for couples or family therapy,** currently 90847 for couples/family therapy or 90846 for family therapy without client present.

▶ **Instead of asking if a plan covers couples therapy,** ask them, "do you cover CPT 90847 and 90846 for this member to treat his diagnosis?" This makes it clear that there is a diagnosed client, and that the session is not aimed at personal growth or couples communication. Remember, though, your first diagnostic intake session will be CPT code 90791 with all new clients.

▶ **While you may not like thinking in terms of "identified client," for billing purposes, you need to choose one.** The member of the couple with the diagnosis is the identified client on the claim. If both partners have diagnoses, either may be the identified client, unless one is clearly the focus of treatment. If both have diagnoses, you may want to choose the one who has primary insurance, or the one with the more severe symptoms (see "Double Coverage," Page 106).

▶ **If doing extended couples or family sessions,** see Extended Sessions, Page 68.

► **If doing couples therapy, and you want to see one member of the couple alone who is not your identified client,** use the CPT code 90846, still listing your identified client on your claim. This means if you met individually once with Jill, her name would not appear on the CMS-1500 form. It is a good idea to first ask the plan if they cover 90846. In another scenario, let's say you are doing couples counseling with Jack and Jill, yet Jill wants an individual session to talk about issues unrelated to Jack. In this case, to bill insurance she must have her own diagnosis, and be identified as the client on the claim for this session, and you would use an individual therapy code such as 90834 or 90837. Do not bill Jack's insurance in a way that gives the impression that Jack was present in your individual session with Jill (ex. using a 90847 CPT code).

► **If both partners have an EAP benefit, and you are seeing them as a couple,** you might be able to bill some sessions under Jack's EAP authorization, and then have Jill get an authorization, so that you could bill the next set under her name. In this way, if each family member has eight EAP sessions, you could do 16 EAP couples sessions. However, it is wise to check with the Employee Assistance Program to be sure this is allowed. Remember that the intention of the EAP program is for assessment, brief treatment, and referral, so two sets of EAP sessions may not be allowed.

► **Can I see two clients from the same family for ongoing individual sessions?** This is usually a clinical decision, left in your hands. Most insurance plans don't specifically forbid it in their policies. If you would like to see two members of the same family individually, and you have a good clinical reason for doing so, document your reasons in the client charts, and talk over the risks and benefits with both members.

Double Coverage: When a Client or Couple is Covered by Two Plans

When a client or couple is covered by two plans, things get complicated. This may happen when both have coverage, or when the identified client is covered by two plans. I have been told conflicting information by different health plans on how this works, but what follows is the most conservative reading of the information I've gotten from my best sources. While the process varies somewhat depending on circumstances, in most cases, you would:

1. Determine whose insurance is "primary" (See "Questions and Answers" Page 109).
2. Collect deductibles and/or copayments as if the primary plan is the only coverage.
3. Submit a claim to the primary plan. If Jack has the diagnosis, and his plan is the primary insurance, identify Jack as the client on the claim, and use the CPT code for a couples session (90847). If using the CMS-1500 claim form, fill in the details about Jill's plan when asked about "other insurance" (boxes 9, 9a, 9d, and 11d).
4. The primary plan will send a payment or denial with an Explanation of Benefits (EOB). This is sent to him, if you are out of network, or to you, if you are in network.
5. Then a claim may be submitted to the secondary insurance plan to try to collect whatever portion the primary plan did not pay. Be sure to <u>include a copy of the primary plan's EOB.</u> The secondary plan (let's say Jill's) may reimburse the couple for whatever their out-of-pocket expenses were for the session (their deductibles and copayments), though sometimes there are limits to secondary coverage.
6. The total amount you or your client collects from the two insurance plans for the session may not exceed your full fee (if you are out-of-network) or your contracted rate (if you are in-network with either plan). If you are paid too much by the secondary plan, the overpayment must be refunded to the secondary plan, or this is fraud. If you are paid in full by the insurance plan you will have to reimburse the clients if they paid you copayments.

Huh?? Let's try some examples.

Jack and Jill are in couples therapy. Only Jack has a diagnosis. Both have health plans (Jack's is CureQuick Health Plan, Jill's is BeWell). Both have out of network benefits. You determine Jack's plan is primary (see Page 109). Let's say your full fee is $100 Jack's plan pays network providers $67, and Jill's plan pays network providers $70. Both plans cover 70% when a client sees a network therapist, and 50% of the UCR (maximum allowed amount) when going to an out-of-network provider. After submitting claims, you find both plans have a UCR of $90. Neither has a deductible.*

	Example 1 You are a Network Provider for Both Plans	Example 2 You're Out-of-Network for Both Plans	Example 3 You're In-Network only for the Primary Plan	Example 4 You're In-Network only for the Secondary Plan
Collect at Session:	$20.10 30% coinsurance of primary plan	$100 (your full fee)	$20.10 30% of $67, your contract rate with primary plan	$100 (your full fee)
Primary Pays: (70% in-network, 50% out-of-network)	$46.90 to you (70% of $67, your contracted rate with the primary plan)	$45 to client (50% of the plan's UCR, in this case $90)	$46.90 to you (70% of $67, your contract rate with the primary plan)	$45 to client (50% of the plan's UCR, in this case $90)
Secondary Pays**: (70% in-network, 50% out-of-network)	$20.10** (this is a refund of the client's coinsurance; refund client if you are paid)	$45 to client (this is what remains after you subtract what the primary plan paid from their out-of-network allowed rate of $90)	$20.10** to client (this is a refund of the client's coinsurance; refund client if you are paid)	$25** (Your $70 contracted rate with the secondary plan minus what primary paid; refund client if you are paid)
Client's Responsibility, After Both Pay:	$0	$10	$0	$30
Total You Can Collect For Session	$67 (your rate with primary)	$100 (your full fee)	$67 (your contract rate with primary plan)	$70 (your contract rate with secondary)
Must I be the one to bill the primary plan?	Yes (It is in your contract with both plans)	No (Since you didn't sign a contract agreeing to do it)	Yes (It is in your contract with this plan to do so)	No (Since you didn't sign a contract agreeing to do it)
Must I be the one to bill the secondary plan?	Yes (It is in your contract with both plans)	No (The couple can -- you didn't sign a contract with any plan to do it)	No (The couple can -- you didn't sign a contract with the secondary to do it)	Yes (It is in your contract, but get the EOB from client)

* Note: This information would change when either plan has a deductible – see Page 110.
**The secondary plan may mistakenly pay more -- you must refund any overpayments.
Chart info confirmed by Susan Frager, LCSW, Owner, Psych Admin Partners billing, psychadminpartners.com

In Example 1, you are a network provider for both plans. Since in our example Jack's is primary, you collect his co-insurance, and then submit a claim to his plan, CureQuick. CureQuick sees your contracted rate is $67, and pays 70 percent of this amount, for a total of $46.90, leaving Jack a co-insurance of $20.10. You may then submit a claim to Jill's insurance, BeWell (you must do the billing, since you agreed to do this in your contract with Jill's plan). Attach a copy of CureQuick's EOB. BeWell pays the difference between your contract rate with the primary plan ($67) and the amount that was paid ($46.90), for a total of $20.10. You are limited to collecting a combined total of $67 (your contracted rate with the primary plan). If the secondary plan pays more than $20.10, you must refund it. You can't bill Jack for any difference between your full fee and your contract rate with the primary plan. And you must refund Jack for any payments he made to you.

In Example 2, you are not a provider for either network. Jack's plan is still primary. Because you are out-of-network, the client should pay you up front. Then when the claim is submitted, CureQuick will reimburse $45, which is 50 percent of $90. Why didn't they pay 50 percent of your full fee $100? $90 is the UCR, which the amount the plan has determined is the maximum payable to out-of-network providers. The couple may then bill Jill's plan, BeWell, attaching a copy of CureQuick's EOB. BeWell should pay the difference between CureQuick's UCR of $90 and the $45 that was already paid, for a total of $45. The good news? As an out-of-network provider, you are not bound by any UCR from either plan, and collect your full fee for the session from the clients even if his insurance plan sets UCRs. It is helpful to tell clients up front (or have a treatment agreement that states) that they owe whatever insurance doesn't pay (see Sample Treatment Agreement, 143).

In Example 3, you are only contracted with the primary plan, CureQuick (Jack's plan). However, you will notice the payments are the same as Example 1. Why? Because in most cases, sessions are processed according to the terms of the primary plan. You collect a co-insurance from Jack, then bill CureQuick. CureQuick will pay $46.90, which is 70 percent of your $67 contract rate, leaving Jack a co-insurance of $20.10. The couple may then bill Jill's plan, BeWell, attaching a copy of CureQuick's EOB. BeWell calculates the difference between your contract rate with the primary plan and the amount the primary paid ($46.90), reimbursing the client for the co-insurance they paid of $20.10. You can't collect more than $67 for this session (your contracted rate with the primary). You may not bill the client for any difference between your full fee and your contract rate with the primary plan.

In Example 4, you are only contracted with Jill's plan, BeWell. Since Jack's plan is the primary, you still need to submit to his plan first. Because you are an out-of-network provider, you can collect your full fee from Jack at the session (which I would recommend, as you don't know if Jack will submit any invoice you give him to the primary plan, much less ask you to submit to the secondary). If he does submit to the primary plan, CureQuick should reimburse him $45, which is 50 percent of $90. Why didn't they pay 50 percent of your full fee $100? In our example, $90 is the UCR, which the amount the plan has determined is the maximum payable to out-of-network providers. If Jack wants you to submit a secondary claim to Jill's insurance, BeWell, he would need to give you a copy of the primary plan's EOB to submit with the claim. BeWell will see that your contract rate with BeWell is $70, and will subtract what the primary plan paid ($45) from $70, and pay the remaining $25. In this case, I believe that since you are contracted with the secondary, and your contract states that you shouldn't accept more than your contracted amount of $70 for the session, you should refund the client the $30 additional they paid for each session that was above your BeWell contract rate. However, this last sentence is the part of all this that I am least certain, as I have had difficulty getting more than one expert to back it up.

Are you thoroughly confused yet?

Questions and Answers

I've looked at your chart and examples, and this is NOT what the insurance plan representatives (or my billing expert) told me about double coverage, or how I've been paid.

I understand. When researching this book, I got all kinds of contradicting information (and downright misinformation) from even high-level folks at different plans. But customer service representatives, clinical case managers, and even network managers are typically not trained about these complicated, in-the-weeds double claims issues, and will often give you bad advice. Even most claims examiners don't know how this all works. This makes it hard for me to be positive even in writing this to you! However, after consulting with enough experts, I believe the information in this chapter is correct. The bottom line? You are accountable for knowing the

terms of any contract you signed with the insurance plan(s), especially your contracted fee, and this is the maximum you can collect for any session if you are in-network with either plan -- no matter what the plan representatives may tell you.

What do I do if the secondary plan pays me too much, or more than my contracted rate? Can I keep the overpayment?

I wish I could say yes, but the answer is no. "You need to reimburse the secondary plan even though it is their mistake. The error is theirs for not looking at the primary [plan's] EOB and noting that there is a contract discount. It's a frequent error," says Psych Admin Service's Susan Frager, a mental health billing expert.[51] "This gets sticky and really requires a claims examiner who knows what he or she is doing...and understands the difference between UCR and contracted rate. Often you get people that don't have a clue, unfortunately," says Frager. Remember, too, that accepting overpayments is fraud, and violates your contract with the plan.

Your examples make it sound like the plans will tell you their UCR up front.

Sometimes they will, sometimes they won't. Why wouldn't they? "They don't want to risk that the provider will inflate their charge. If you call, you may be told only that your billed charge is within their UCR, or is above it. So, you end up having to wait for the first claim to come back to know what the UCR is," says Frager. And this is one reason I recommend you bill soon after a client's first session. However, it is worth asking on the first call, by asking "is my fee of $XXX within your UCR?" Remember, UCRs are only something that affects out-of-network providers, since rates are already set for network providers.

Let's say Jack is covered by two plans (for example, because he works two jobs, or has his own plan and is a dependent on Jill's plan). Which is the primary insurance?

If only Jack has a diagnosis, he is the identified client. If Jack is covered by two insurance plans, and is the primary subscriber on his (CureQuick) plan and the dependent on another (say his wife's plan, BeWell), the plan where he is the primary subscriber or policyholder is considered the primary insurance.

If Jack is the primary policyholder on more than one plan, you may need to check the effective dates. In most cases, the plan that has covered Jack the longest would be designated as his primary insurance. If both plans have the same effective date, the primary plan may be the one with the earliest date of hire (that is, where he has worked longest). But this varies by insurance plan, so call and ask.

What if both partners have diagnoses and their own plans? Whose is primary?

If one is covered as the subscriber or policyholder on his/her plan, and the other is covered as a dependent (e.g., if Jill is covered by her parents' plan), the policyholder's plan will be the primary one. If both are policyholders on their own policies, and both have diagnoses, the "birthday rule" often applies. This means (according to two plan representatives I spoke to) that the primary insurance may be that of the client whose birthday falls earliest in the year (not necessarily the older person). No, I'm not kidding. But in some plans, the primary is the one that has provided the longest coverage. Obviously, this varies with insurance plan, so call the insurance plans involved and discuss your specific case at the start of therapy.

What if my identified client is a dependent child, covered by both parents' plans?

Again, this varies by the company. One insurance company representative I spoke with stated that if both parents are the primary subscribers on their own coverage, the plan of the parent whose birthday falls earlier in the year (remember, not necessarily the older parent) is the primary. If the parents have the same birthday, the primary plan may be the one who has provided coverage longer, or to the plan of the parent whose first name begins with an earlier alphabet letter! I am not making this up. Some plans may simply have the father as the primary carrier. However, this might not be the case if the parents are divorced or separated, where benefits are typically first billed to the custodial parent's plan first, and in cases of joint custody, the birthday rule typically applies. Now you see why you must call the plans involved in your case.

What if the primary plan has a copayment of $25 and no deductible, and the secondary plan has a copayment of $35. Which do I collect?

After determining which plan is primary, follow the terms of this coverage. In this case, that means you would collect the $25 copayment. However, Jack may be able to seek reimbursement of this $25 from his secondary plan. See the chart earlier in this Chapter.

If I provide couples therapy, can I bill both partners' insurance for an individual therapy session?

No. The CPT codes are different (90847 couples code vs. 90834 or 90837 individual). This would be misrepresenting the service provided, which is insurance fraud. This might also seem as if you are trying to collect your full fee from each plan, which is also fraud. If you want to bill two insurance plans for the same couples therapy session, you would need to bill the primary plan first, and the secondary insurance after the primary has paid. You must also include on the claim the details about the other partner's coverage, as described on Pages 62-63, and Page 106. For more on insurance fraud, see Chapter 16.

What if the client has a deductible for either plan?

Collect as you would if there was only the primary coverage. If you are a network provider you should collect your contracted rate for the sessions until the primary plan's deductible is exhausted. You still need to submit your claim to help the client to use up the deductible, and you (or the client, if you are out of network) still need to submit the claim or invoice so that you can get the Explanation of Benefits (EOB), which you need if seeking reimbursement from the secondary plan.

The secondary plan did not pay the way you suggested they would in your chart.

Depending on how the plan is written, secondary plans may vary a great deal on coverage. Unlike my chart, some secondary plans will not pay anything more for the session. In cases like our example where the client has similar coverage levels to the primary insurance, the secondary may argue that what the primary paid was close to or more than what they would have paid, so no additional payment is due. In other cases, the secondary will pay but won't reimburse the client in full for his copayments -- for example, if the secondary plan has 70% coverage, they might reimburse 70% of the client's copayments.

This sounds like a lot of work and makes my head ache. Can I just collect the copayment or co-insurance from my client, bill the primary insurance plan, and leave it to Jack to try to collect from his secondary insurance plan?

I understand completely. Just writing this section makes my head ache, also! However, as it shows in the examples on Page 107 and 108, if you are a network provider with the primary or secondary plan, you have agreed to take care of billing for the client for that plan.

If you are not responsible for billing the secondary plan, you may educate Jill about the process and give her the necessary documentation to submit, including a copy of the EOB from the primary insurance showing what they paid for the sessions. Be sure she gets the proper claim form from their employer or insurance plan (or help her fill out the CMS-1500).

This seems incredibly complicated!

You get no argument here. Sometimes, this makes the idea of having a mental health billing service (one that is knowledgeable about this area) very attractive. But having to bill two insurance plans may not happen as often as you may think. And rest assured: In my mind this is the most complicated aspect of working with insurance. If you understand this, everything else will be a cake-walk!

18

Life as a Network Provider:
Profiles, Audits, Records, Raises, & Resignations

❧ ❧

What's Expected of You?

While expectations vary from between networks, here are some expectations that are fairly universal among insurance plans:

▶ **Keep excellent progress notes.** Not only is it your best defense in case of a client complaint to a licensing board or ethics committee, but insurance plans are reviewing provider charts more than in the past, for a host of reasons (if you haven't already done so, read the section on What Should be in Your Progress Notes—And Probably Isn't, on Page 54).

▶ **You'll need a treatment plan.** Most plans will want you to have a written treatment plan in each chart. Some states even require a treatment plan. However, it is unlikely that a plan will ever ask to see your plan unless your chart is reviewed.

▶ **Return client calls promptly,** usually within one business day. "One of the biggest complaints we get from clients is that providers never call them back, even established clients," one insurance network manager shared.

▶ **Coordinate care with other treating clinicians and physicians.** Insurance plans will look for this if they audit your charts or review your treatment. Discuss the importance of this communication with clients, especially if the client is taking psychiatric medications, has a significant medical condition or substance abuse disorder, has a major mental illness, is violent, has difficulty following doctor's recommendations, or was referred to you by the doc. Make every attempt to obtain the client's signed release, and always record a client's refusals. MHN reports 68% of the provider charts they audited lacked evidence of coordination with a treating medical practitioner (or of refusal by the client).[52]

▶ **If treating a child or adolescent, involve parents in treatment, when possible.**

▶ **Let the insurance company know about any changes** in your demographic information, including address, phone number, specialty, Tax ID number, or name.

- **Send the insurance company copies of your license and malpractice insurance renewals.** Be sure you do not let either lapse even briefly during treatment.

- **Let the plan know if you will be unable to take referrals** due to vacation, leave, a full practice, or personal issues. This may even be mandated by state law.

- **Don't speak negatively to the client about the insurance plan.** In the contract you signed with the plan, you may have even agreed not to criticize the company to the member. In addition, it is not professional, and may come back to haunt you if the client repeats your comments to the plan. I once foolishly told a potential client I was not taking new clients from her plan while I renegotiated my fee, which I felt was too low. The client repeated this to her plan, and I got a scolding from the plan.

- **Don't "balance-bill" clients** for the difference between your contracted rate and your full fee. This is a violation of your contract if you are a network a provider.

- **Don't tell clients, "my insurance slots are full, but I can see you for full fee."** In your contract with the plan you agreed to accept all their members for the discounted rate. In addition, giving differential access to private pay clients may leave you vulnerable for a client complaint to the plan – or worse, your licensing board or professional association ethics committee.

- **Leave emergency instructions on your voicemail greeting.** If you have no answering service, give clients the number of a crisis hotline, and instruct crisis clients to go to an emergency room or dial 911.

Provider-Profiling

In its broadest definition, "provider-profiling" refers to the information an insurance company keeps on providers. However, to many providers it calls to mind the concept of something more sinister: The sense that Big Brother is looking over our shoulder with a clipboard.

What is in a provider profile? The information differs at each insurance plan, and they don't like to tell us what information they keep on file. The information may include client complaint and client satisfaction data, clinical quality/outcomes data, utilization data (e.g., the average number of sessions per case, possibly even per diagnosis), the results of appointment accessibility surveys, and the results of site visit evaluations and treatment record reviews that may have taken place.

Feeling worried? Don't panic. Insurance companies recognize that some clients have more severe problems than others, not all clients are going to love you, and that some clients are just plain difficult. They are looking for repeating patterns that are outside the expectations they have of providers (ex. if your average length of treatment for all your clients is unusually long, or your number of sessions per week is abnormally high).

Getting More Client Referrals --- Or Less

Here are a few tips to increase the flow of insurance clients:

- **Call the insurance company and ask about your current network status.** See if there has been a computer "glitch" that has kept you from getting more referrals. You may have been accidentally removed from the network or placed into "limbo-listing." This is when you have not been terminated from the network, but you have somehow lost your active status, perhaps because you failed to update some paperwork.

- ► **Is your information current?** Call the plan's provider relations or network management department to make sure your contact info, specialties, and address are up to date.

- ► **Check what potential clients are seeing on the online provider directory.** If the insurance plan has a website, pretend you are a potential client, and see if you come up when you search the provider directory in your area. If so, are you listed as "active," or "taking new clients?" Is your other information correct? Also, does the site offer the opportunity to post a provider profile, listing your specialties or a personal statement? Some health plans (like CIGNA) allow you to provide a provider profile and personal statement to describe your practice and your treatment philosophy in your own words. Use this space to sell yourself. Get feedback on your profile. Upload a picture, if possible.

- ► **Tell the plan if you are able to provide special services.** If you are able to provide telehealth, make your health plans aware of this. Some insurance companies will make more referrals (or even pay more) to therapists willing to see clients in special situations, such as Crisis Stabilization / emergency referrals, or accepting new clients who have just been discharged from the hospital (or are about to be). Being able to provide Critical Incident Stress Debriefings (CISD) or teach employer-requested trainings or lectures might also get you referrals. You might also tell the plan if you are available on weekends.

- ► **Create your own website where potential clients can learn more about you, and be sure to list the insurance plans you accept.** As was mentioned earlier, research indicates the majority of clients now search online before contacting a therapist. This means that no matter where Jack gets your name (even if he gets it from your insurance plan's website), he is likely to enter your name into his Internet search engine to research and compare you with other therapists whose names are on his list. If he can't find you, or your website is just ho-hum, he will likely go on to the next name, and you will have lost a client. Creating a profile on the PsychologyToday.com online directory may be a simple first step.

Most therapist websites are too clinical, talking about education and experience. It is important that the client be able to "hear your voice," and get a feeling for what it will be like to be in the room with you. Speak in plain language and warm words.

- ► **Get more training.** Becoming a Certified Employee Assistance Professional (CEAP) or obtaining a Substance Abuse Professional (SAP) qualification could help you get on EAP plans, get more referrals, and sometimes increase your reimbursement rate. Getting training in EMDR and other specialized treatment might, also.

- ► **Distribute referral lists to area physicians, hospitals, clinics, and therapists.** The therapists in my building have a shared referral list, where --- in addition to seeing specialties, hours, and fees --- we can see who among us is a provider for any given insurance network. This has proved a very effective referral tool for all of us.

- ► **Be sure you are on the list for all the company's plans.** Perhaps you joined the PPO plan but were not automatically placed on the HMO or EAP network provider list.

- ► **The no-brainer:** Call and ask the insurance company what you might do to get more referrals. They may be aware of their needs.

What if you want to stop the flow of clients? Call provider relations and ask to be put on "inactive status" for a period of time; just be sure to contact them when you would like to begin receiving referrals again. Remember, if you go on inactive status for too long you might get a call from the plan -- they don't want you on the panel if you aren't going to be open for members for long stretches.

Audits and Records Requests

From time to time, insurance companies audit (review) client medical records and may even visit providers offices to be sure files are being kept in a professional manner, to review a case for a reimbursement decision, or to help maintain the quality of care.

Often, I get a phone call from a panicked therapist, saying "help! I'm being audited!" In fact, only a small number of them are being audited. They may be confused about a letter they got from the insurance plan.

Why would a plan ask for records?

- ▶ **A "medical necessity" review.** As discussed earlier, a treatment review is when the plan is seeking more information to see if it considers treatment medically necessary. It is rare for insurance plans to ask for notes, but they could (for more about medical necessity, see Chapter 9).

- ▶ **An audit.** This is typically more a review of the provider's documentation. They are checking for your compliance with the plan's administrative expectations, and is not about your treatment. Typically, the plan will ask you to send copies of a few charts.

- ▶ **To comply with the Affordable Care Act Risk Adjustment provision.** Here, progress notes are requested not for the purposes of reviewing your treatment or how you keep charts, but instead to gain more in-depth information about diagnoses, symptom severity, and medical history for statistical purposes. This helps determine the amount of Risk Adjustment payments that plans are required to make to other health plans based on the relative health of their members. In this form of annual balancing, plans covering "healthier" members will have to make payments to those plans covering "sicker" members.

Questions and Answers

Why might I be selected for an audit? All insurance plans have standards they have to meet to get approval from their own credentialing agencies. As part of their own quality assurance measures, they must pick a certain number of providers each year and conduct a review of the provider's office procedures and files. So, you may be chosen randomly, you may be selected because you have a home office, because you see clients in their homes, or because you are a "high-volume provider." Or you may have been identified as an "outlier," in that your coding or billing practices have been identified by the plan's computer algorithm software tools as indicating conduct that is unusual or outside the norm of your provider peers. Examples include when you see clients for multiple sessions each week, when you regularly bill for multiple sessions in a day, or when you use extended session codes more frequently than your colleagues.

But you may never get audited, or you may go years between audits. <u>In my 30 years as an insurance provider for more than 15 networks, I have never been formally audited</u> (am I tempting the audit gods by publicizing that?).

How can I prepare? The good news is that an audit doesn't have to be a blind ambush. As was mentioned earlier, you can usually get a list (usually in the provider manual) of what the plan would like to see in your notes and charts. Larger insurance companies often have a copy of these requirements on their websites, and some even have an "audit checklist" so you know ahead of time what they would expect if they were ever to audit you. The company will usually give you warning of the audit, and resend the list of requirements.

While it is tempting to "clean up your files" (rewrite progress notes, or write notes you never wrote) before a site visit, resist the urge. This is unethical, and you could be guilty of fraud. This is another reason it is important to write notes each day as if you will be audited tomorrow. (Check out my webinar on What Should be in Your Client Charts, see Resources, Page 133)

Do I need the client's written consent from my client for a documentation audit? In your contract, you likely agreed to cooperate with the plan's administrative reviews. However, "it is best to get the client's written consent – some states require a patient's written consent in order to review mental health records, even in an audit," says Dave Jensen, a mental health attorney.[53] And a client's signature on the CMS-1500 claim form may not be enough. "Mental health has a higher standard of privacy than medical, and this particular release has been challenged in court, since it does not measure up to release requirements outlined by HIPAA," says Jensen. "And while the request may tell you HIPAA states a client release is not required, state laws around client privacy may supersede federal HIPAA regulations if the state has more rigorous standards."

Do I have to release all my notes? Just the ones that are requested. But Keep in mind that if you are a HIPAA-covered entity, and you keep psychotherapy notes separate from your progress notes, they should be protected from insurance plan audits (for further details about the different types of notes, see Page 34).

What if I was providing couples or family therapy? Do I need a release from all members who were being seen? It is wise, and may be legally mandated, to get the signed permission of all therapy participants prior to releasing notes to anyone. Get legal advice.

What if I'm an out-of-network provider? As was mentioned earlier, even if you are out-of-network and Jack submits your invoice, he is opening his files to possible evaluation by the health plan. But for some administrative records reviews, you may have received the request in error. Call to be sure.

So, what should I do if I'm asked for records? This will depend on the purpose of the request. Here are some general tips to consider:

> **1. Contact the plan.** Find out what they want and why. If being audited, ask the plan for their audit checklist. (If a treatment review, see Chapter 9).
>
> **2. Try to create middle ground.** "Find a way to give them what they need but release as little as possible, and still maintain confidentiality," says Jensen. "See if they will accept a treatment summary." Don't give any more pages or dates of service than are requested.
>
> **3. Talk to the client,** explaining the purpose of the audit, and how they feel about it. Get a written release from your client, or – if this is just a general audit -- see if the plan will accept a "redacted" copy of your records (where all identifying information has been crossed-out or deleted).

4. If the records request is for a treatment review, and the client doesn't want you to release records, tell the plan you are reluctant or unwilling to release records without the client's signed release. Of course, you should explain to your client that the plan may not approve more sessions without this review.

5. Try to relax. While administrative audits can be anxiety-provoking, remember the goal of the audit is quality improvement, not punishment. Also, you need not meet 100% of their expectations to achieve a passing score.

6. If you've been contacted for a treatment review, call the plan and ask what questions you should prepare for. Read the section of this book about Medical Necessity (Chapter 9), prepare carefully by rereading the client's chart, and get consultation to lower your anxiety and figure out how to best advocate for your client's care (for the name of consultants, see Resources, Page 133).

Colleagues who have gone through administrative audits tell me they are not the hellish encounters they dreaded. And if you don't pass, the plan will typically give you feedback about improvements they would like to see, and give you a chance to change your ways. Many items they are looking for are just good practice, so it is a good opportunity to start some good charting habits after the audit.

Getting a Raise

It will come as no surprise that in one survey of therapists, network providers' biggest complaint about insurance was the low reimbursement rate.[54] Despite the fact that this is our biggest sore point, the survey reflected that 61% of respondents had never attempted to negotiate an increase in their contracted rate with an insurance plan. Many therapists are not even aware that raises are possible. Others feel the chance of getting one is low.

Yet the survey also showed that of those therapists who had attempted to negotiate a reimbursement rate, 40% were successful. So, what have you got to lose?

Over the years I have been able to negotiate several raises for myself (even once when joining a plan), and I have been able to help therapists to get raises.

> ▶ **If you have a colleague who tells you she contacted a plan and wasn't able to get a raise, don't let that deter you.** Or if a colleague tells you they got a raise, don't expect one. Unless it is an across the board fee increase, raises are judged very individually.

> ▶ **Call the plan's Provider Relations Department** and ask how to go about making your request. Be prepared to defend why you feel you deserve a raise, in case they want to discuss it on the call. If you are told no fee increases are being given, insist that you want to request one, and ask for the address and to whom you should address your request. Ask if you can fax or email it, and if there is anything you should include in your request.

> ▶ **What to highlight in your request:** Let them know why you are worth paying a bit more to keep. Include how long you have been with the network, whether you are a high-volume provider, and your unique specialties or skills. It isn't enough that you do couples therapy, or treat anxiety or depression -- so do most other therapists.
> Let them know if you can offer therapy in another language (if this is the case, you might even be able to negotiate a raise when joining), provide crisis stabilization or emergency care, post-hospitalization discharge visits, weekend hours, or if you treat kids, Autism/Asperger's, ADHD, veterans, the hearing-impaired, if you have experience with chemical dependency, eating disorders, trauma, chronic pain/illness,

veteran's issues, if you provide EMDR, or if you are a Certified Employee Assistance Professional (CEAP) or Substance Abuse Professional (SAP).

Tell them if you provide telehealth, and highlight how this enables you to provide services for their members statewide, including underserved areas. In addition, emphasize if you work in an underserved area where plans need therapists, if you are a minority or a male therapist (plans need a diverse therapist base) or if you are part of a group practice that can offer a continuum of services. Once when joining an EAP plan, I was able to get a higher rate when I told them I had done Critical Incident Stress Debriefings in the past, and had provided wellness lectures at employer sites and Mandatory Employer Trainings on Sexual Abuse and Substance Abuse. But don't assume if you have a general practice you can't get a raise. Just put your best foot forward, and ask (see "Letters of Interest" Page 22 for other ideas of what to highlight in your raise request letter).

▶ **List the CPT codes for your services and the rates you are requesting for each.** I usually suggest you ask for a $20 increase in your current rates.

▶ **Consider collecting data on your practice.** You may want to be able to give statistics about your average number of sessions per client, or results of client satisfaction surveys or client improvement questionnaires.

▶ **Avoid whining** about your costs and economic realities, or sounding resentful. You may want to briefly mention how long you have been on the network without a raise, but for try to focus on what makes you worth the added dollars.

▶ **Don't threaten to quit** if you don't get what you want. You may, however, hint you are unsure if you can continue at the current rate.

▶ **You may want to hire an insurance consultant** to help you craft your rate request, and tailor it to your specific situation, so you make the most persuasive argument and to get sample raise-requests letters (for consultants, see Resources, Page 133).

▶ **If you are unsuccessful, try again in six months.**

Can We Fight Together For Raises?

Mental health attorneys advise that self-employed health care professionals cannot collectively bargain for better contracts or better reimbursement rates – only therapists who are employees and who hold non-managerial positions can organize a union to collectively negotiate. Therapists in private practice and others who are self-employed are independent contractors, and cannot boycott or strike, or threaten as a group to resign if reimbursement rates are not increased. This is considered "price fixing" or "restraint of trade," and violates
the Sherman Anti-trust Act of 1890.[55] The health plan needs only to establish that there has been some sort of "contract, combination, or conspiracy" between you and other healthcare professionals in an effort to collectively bargain and control reimbursement rates. Attorney

and physician Weldon Havins writes, "such an agreement does not need to be in writing or be part of a formal agreement. A simple, informal discussion between competing [providers] at a social function expressing dissatisfaction about an HMO's payment schedule, followed by a mass withdrawal of [providers] from an HMO could support a successful anti-trust prosecution. Truly independent competing [providers] … attempting to negotiate jointly for payment rates from third-party payers may be engaging in prohibited concerted activity."[56.] He warns that "a [provider] should never, even if only acting independently, use the threat of collaborative action to enhance his bargaining power

According to several anti-trust experts I interviewed, even comparing reimbursement rates over coffee with a group of therapists or participating in an online chatroom conversation to brainstorm what actions could be taken to affect reimbursement rates could potentially put you in hot water. This may trigger an investigation, especially if the health plan sees a number of therapists taking the same action. If the health plan can prove that there was some meeting, communication, or agreement between the therapists involved, the consequences can be severe. This is a felony, and the Act states that "…if convicted, you "shall be punished by a fine not exceeding … $350,000, or by imprisonment not exceeding three years, or both."[57]

Many providers are frustrated that their professional organizations do not actively fight plans for raises on their behalf. This is why they can't.

Resigning

If the reason you are leaving the plan is financial, you might ask the plan for a raise before you leave. But if you choose to resign, you are typically contractually obligated to give written notice of resignation to the plan. 60 - 120 days' written notice is usually required Check your contract. Call the plan to ask where to send your resignation, and in the letter give them an effective date of the resignation (be sure it conforms to the advance notice requirement).

It's wise to fax your resignation, email it, and also send it by a mail service and that will give you proof of receipt. Then ask the plan to hold new referrals, listing you as "inactive" or "not accepting new clients" in their database and on the website.

You are ethically bound to transition your clients in a professional manner, and to collaborate in their referral. if needed. I recommend you give a letter to all clients who are affected by your resignation, announcing the effective date that you will no longer be a network provider, outlining what this means for them, and what their options are. These options include ending treatment, transitioning to a network provider or community provider, or continuing to see you but paying privately. Some of your clients may be able to seek reimbursement for your services if they have out of network benefits. Keep a copy of this letter in their chart. The insurance plan will often send a letter to past and present clients to let them know you are resigning. So that your resignation is not a surprise, tell current clients before they get the letter from the plan.

19

"Should I Accept Insurance?"

❧ ☙

A Self-Quiz

Here are some questions to help you evaluate whether to join a network:

1. **What are your practice goals?** What kinds of clients do you like working with? How often would you like to be able to see them? Can the population you want to work with afford to pay you out of pocket for this amount of sessions per month? If not, what options do you have for enabling these clients to see you, and how do you feel about these other options?

2. **What are your income needs?** How many hours a week do you plan to work, and how much money do you need to make? You may decide you can't afford to discount your fee in order to join a network, even for a few insurance clients. Crunch the numbers, with different scenarios, from ones where you see a few insurance clients to ones where you see a lot of insurance clients. Joining too many plans may mean too many discounted therapy slots.

3. **What is your cash flow situation?** Can you handle waiting several weeks after a session for insurance payments?

4. **Is private-pay-only working for you?** If you have a number of empty therapy slots you'd like to fill, accepting insurance might be worth considering. Becoming a network provider may bring a steady stream of referrals, which may be very helpful in building or filling out your practice. Perhaps you'd rather collect $70-$100 for an insurance client than collect nothing for an unfilled hour.

5. **How do you feel about advertising?** Do you loathe self-promotion? Have you been doing advertising, and it hasn't helped as much as you would like? Is it costing you more than you want to spend? Becoming a network provider can cut down on your need to advertise. As a network provider, insurance plans put your name on their provider lists on their websites, and they give

out your name to their members who call for referrals. I currently get three to four calls and emails a day from clients who got my name from their insurance plan, which has significantly reduced my need to do outside advertising – other than a professional website, which is essential (review my argument for this, Page 117).

6. **Are you losing clients because they need to choose a provider on their plan?** Accepting insurance can mean retaining the clients you enjoy working with, and not being forced to turn away new clients who need to use their benefits.

7. **What's your attitude toward insurance?** Evaluate your countertransference before joining. Would you resent the idea of a case manager calling to review a case? Would you be tempted to speak negatively to your clients about insurance? Would you resent your reimbursement rate? Would you feel like a victim of insurance? Many providers seem to spend their whole time on the panel chafing at the terms of the agreement they signed. If after reading this manual you are still very negatively inclined toward insurance, you might want to stay away from participation.

8. **What is your attitude toward short-term therapy?** It isn't necessary to restrict yourself to short-term therapy if you work with insurance. I have seen many clients for years (one seriously mentally ill client even for decades). However, shorter-term, symptom-focused therapy is the heart and soul of what insurance plans want, and you need to be comfortable with this work. If what you do is in-depth psychoanalysis with your clients, meeting several times a week, or if you'd resist having any kind of goals or treatment plan for the client, working within an insurance framework may not be right for you.

9. **What level of involvement might work for you?** It may be helpful to review Chapter 2, and your options for participation. How do you feel about becoming involved with each type of plan? You might start out slowly, by joining one plan, just to see how this feels. Then perhaps you could consider joining additional networks. Remember, you can always resign any network should you choose not to continue.

10. **Are you reasonably organized?** While you don't need to be obsessive-compulsive to be a good provider, organization is important. Claims must be filed in a timely manner, and you must keep track of payments to be sure none slip between the cracks. You may have to keep on top of authorization numbers, expiration dates, and amount of sessions used. This may sound daunting at first, but most providers quickly devise their own organization system (see Sample Service Record, Page 147). Keep a folder for each plan you work with, with copies of the contract, correspondence from the plan, your contracted rate for each CPT code with that plan, claims addresses, contact information, and notes about the basics of what is expected.

11. **Do you keep good case notes and records?** Or at least, are you willing to start? I can't stress the importance of this enough. You may never have had to turn over your notes to a third party, but this is happening more often than ever before. While all therapists need good notes (and it is mandated by most state laws and/or professional ethical standards), it is doubly important for insurance providers because of the possibility of insurance plan audits or medical necessity treatment review. (If you don't keep notes, aren't confident about the notes you keep, or don't know what should be in your notes, see the section on notes on Page 54; for more helpful

tips and sample progress notes and templates check out my Progress Notes webinar, "What Should Be In Your Client Charts—And Probably Isn't; Writing Great Progress Notes and Treatment Plans," see Resources, Page 134).

12. **Do you resent paperwork?**   At the very minimum, working as a network provider will mean submitting claim forms. You may be providing clients with HIPAA Privacy Policies,   Depending on the plan, paperwork may include statements of understanding (treatment agreements provided by the insurance plan), client questionnaires required by the plan, treatment authorization requests, and recredentialing paperwork. You will also need to keep track of the insurance plan's coverage details for each client, and keep track of EOBs and claims payment. If you hate paperwork, you may choose not to become a network provider, or simply avoid those plans with high paperwork requirements, or limit the number of insurance clients you accept. Or you might hire a billing service to do some of this for you (see Billing Service Resources, in Resources, Page 133).

Don't try to fit into a "shoe that doesn't fit." Taking insurance is not for everyone.

Taking Care of Yourself: The Secrets of Insurance Sanity

I'd be lying if I said that working with insurance is an easy path. Most things in life get more complicated when a third party is involved, and therapy is no different. However, if you do choose to become an insurance provider, here are a few self-care tips:

▶ **Balance your insurance and private-pay clients.** Belonging to too many insurance plans can mean that a high percentage of your clients are insurance clients. This can mean you are not collecting your full fee very often – even though many of these clients might have been able to pay your full fee had you not been on their plan. If your therapy slots are filled by insurance clients, you may end up taking an uncomfortable income cut due to the high number of discounted rates. Also, the more insurance clients you have, the more time you spend doing paperwork, and the more time on the phone unsnarling claim problems.

▶ **Avoid reacting to those who bad-mouth insurance providers.** There is an unspoken attitude you may experience from some therapists who have a private-pay-only practice, something like, "I'm a real therapist – I'm not selling out our profession to insurance plans." Another version: "I don't accept insurance because I know I am worth my fee -- insurance providers don't have good self-esteem, and don't feel they deserve their full fee." Take a few deep breaths, and don't internalize these attitudes.

▶ **Consult with other therapists who accept insurance.** Having regular consultation is especially recommended for those working with insurance. There are unique challenges involved with being a network provider, and it is helpful to have the support of other therapists who are familiar with these challenges.

- ► **Avoid overly negative providers.** While misery loves company, and it is natural to complain about insurance, negativity doesn't help.

- ► **Try to verify advice you get form colleagues.** The unfortunate truth is there is a lot of misinformation floating around that many providers pass along as truth. Act like a journalist and verify all information.

- ► **Don't allow resentment about the fees to affect your work.** Get what support you need to make peace with the fees, or else request a "raise"(see Raises, Page 118).

- ► **Consider resigning if the resentment is too great.** Contact the plan to find out their resignation policies, and how much advance notice you need to give (it may be as much as 90 - 120 days), where and how you should mail your resignation letter, and other details about transitioning your clients (for more on resignations, see Page 120).

A Final Question

"Barbara, knowing what you know now, would you still become as involved with insurance?"

Looking back now on the important decisions I've made in my life -- getting married, buying a house, adopting my daughter, and even writing a book -- I'm glad I didn't know how much work each would take before I started. I might have steered away from them completely.

If I had read a book like this before I got involved in insurance, would it have seemed too complicated or too daunting? Probably so. But every payoff has its price. Just because something can be frustrating doesn't mean it should be avoided.

Success in working with insurance requires vision and balance. It helps to have a clear vision of what you want to create for yourself in your life and your practice, and it is important to balance the number of private-pay and insurance clients to achieve that vision. Too many insurance clients can mean working twice as hard for the same pay, leave you ripe for resentment about paperwork and discounts, and leave no room in your practice for full fee clients when they contact you.

However, I am passionate about finding ways to keep our services affordable to the people who may need them most, not just the most affluent among us. Yes, my participation has helped shield me from income fluctuations that can come from empty therapy hours, and has provided me with a steady stream of clients. But more importantly, I look at it as a kind of economic justice, a way of keeping my door open to people of every income level. This means I get the honor of working with ethnically and racially diverse clients from all walks of life. I challenge all of you to find ways to make what we do more financially accessible to a wider range of people. *S*

So, I firmly believe that – even knowing what I know now -- I would still choose to become involved in insurance. But ask me again tomorrow. Depending on the day's insurance frustrations, I might have a different answer!

Endnotes

1. "CAMFT's 2017 Demographic Survey," A Snapshot of the 'Typical' California MFT, Clinical Survey," The California Association of Marriage and Family Therapists, accessed June 27, 2020, https://www.camft.org/Portals/0/PDFs/Demographic-surveys/2017/ClinicalSurvey.pdf?ver=2019-07-10-103433-993
2. "Not White, Not Rich, Ad Seeking Therapy," The Atlantic, June 1 2016, accessed June 27, 2020, https://www.theatlantic.com/health/archive/2016/06/the-struggle-of-seeking-therapy-while-poor/484970/
3. Matej Mikulic, "Health Center Payments in the U.S. 2018 by Insurance, Statistica.com, Feb 6, 2020. Accessed June 27, 2020, https://www.statista.com/statistics/754580/health-center-patients-in-us-by-insurance-status/
4. Casey Truffo, MFT author of *Be a Wealthy Therapist, Finally You Can Make a Living While Making a Difference*, from a posting on *Psychologytoday.com* online bulletin board, June 1, 2006 (used with permission).
5. "EAPs benefit employers, employees: Study," Benefits Canada, February 19, 2014. Assessed June 27, 2020, http://www.benefitscanada.com/benefits/health-wellness/eaps-benefit-employers-employees-study-49686
6. "Assisting an EAP Member in Crisis," *MHN News You Can Use* (Spring, 2006), p. 4.
7. Value Options Provider Manual, Appendix 5, Employee Assistance Program Handbook, , [online]accessed June 27, 2020, http://www.valueoptions.com/providers/Handbook/ValueOptions_Provider_Handbook_Appendix_5.pdf
8. Author correspondence from Gayle W Neill, Director Provider Relations at Value Options/Beacon Health Options, dated July 16, 2015.
9. Managed Health Network Recredentialing paperwork 2006 (author's copy).
10. Humana Employee Assistance Plan (EAP), assessed June 27, 2020, https://www.humana.com/provider/medical-resources/clinical/health-programs/employee-assistance-program
11. EAPA Guidelines, quoted in "Following are a Few FAQs...," *MHN News You Can Use* (Spring, 2005), p. 2.
12. Beacon Health Options Employee Assistance Program Formal or Mandatory Referral, EAP Participant Statement of Understanding, accessed online July 27, 2020, https://www.beaconhealthoptions.com/pdf/eap/H204B.pdf
13. *Provider Access Standards*, Anthem Blue Cross/Blue Shield Provider Manual, accessed June 27, 2020, https://www11.anthem.com/provider/noapplication/f0/s0/t0/pw_e211201.pdf?refer=ahp provider
14. OPTUM Behavioral Health Home Office Audit Tool, accessed June 27, 2020, https://www.providerexpress.com/content/dam/ope-provexpr/us/pdfs/adminResourcesMain/forms/auditTools/homeOfficeAuditTool.pdf
15. "Mental Health Parity," California Hospital Association, assessed June 28, 2020, https://www.calhospital.org/mental-health-parity
16. David Jensen, "Are You a Covered Entity?" Updated August 2010 [online]; accessed June 28, 2020, https://www.camft.org/Resources/Legal-Articles/Chronological-Article-List/are-you-a-covered-entity
17. Phone conversation with Michael Griffin, staff attorney, California Assn. of Marriage and Family Therapists, September 17, 2007.
18. "*Enforcement Results by Year,*" U.S. Dept. of Health and Human Services, accessed June 27, 2020. https://www.hhs.gov/hipaa/for-professionals/compliance-enforcement/data/top-five-issues-investigated-cases-closed-corrective-action-calendar-year/index.html

19. "*Enforcement Results by Year,*" U.S. Dept. of Health and Human Services, accessed June 27, 2020. https://www.hhs.gov/hipaa/for-professionals/compliance-enforcement/data/top-five-issues-investigated-cases-closed-corrective-action-calendar-year/index.html

20. "Notification of Enforcement Discretion for Telehealth Remote Communications During the COVID-19 Nationwide Public Health Emergency." U.S. Dept of Health and Human Services, accessed June 28, 2020, https://www.hhs.gov/hipaa/for-professionals/special-topics/emergency-preparedness/notification-enforcement-discretion-telehealth/index.html

21. "*How the Internet Changed the Way New Patients Find a Physician,*" Patient Pop, March 8, 2018; assessed online June 27, 2020, https://www.patientpop.com/blog/running-a-practice/internet-new-ways-patients-find-physicians

22. Legislative Counsel, State of California. "Confidentiality of Medical Information Act: California Civil Code, Section 56.10" assessed June 28, 2020, http://irb.ucsd.edu/CMIA.pdf

23. American Medical Association, *Current Procedural Terminology 2020, Standard Edition* (Chicago: American Medical Association Press, 2020).

24. American Psychiatric Association, *Diagnostic and Statistical Manual of Mental Disorders DSM-5,* (American Psychiatric Publishing, Washington, D.C. 2012)

25. Susan Frager, *Successful Private Practice: Winning Strategies for Mental Health Professionals* (New York: Wiley, 2000), p. 133.

26. American Medical Association, *ICD-10-CM 2018: International Classification of Diseases* (Chicago: American Medical Association Press, 2018)

27. American Psychiatric Association, *Diagnostic and Statistical Manual of Mental Disorders DSM-5,* (American Psychiatric Publishing, Washington, D.C. 2012)

28. Frager, *Successful Private Practice,* p. 152.

29. "Anthem Blue Cross Blue Shield, Commercial Reimbursement Policy, Subject: Documentation Guidelines for Psychotherapy Services, " effective 7/13/2018, assessed June 28, 2020 https://www11.anthem.com/provider/noapplication/f0/s0/t0/pw_g377388.pdf?refer=ah pmedprovider

30. U.S. Dept. of Labor, "FAQs on COBRA Continuation Health Coverage" [online]; accessed December 6, 2017, https://www.dol.gov/sites/default/files/ebsa/about-ebsa/our-activities/resource-center/faqs/cobra-continuation-health-coverage-consumer.pdf

31. Brad Lotterman, quoted in *Psychotherapy Finances* (December, 2006).

32. American Medical Association, *Current Procedural Terminology 2018 Standard Edition* (Chicago: American Medical Association Press, 2018).

33. National Uniform Claim Committee, "Insurance Claim Form Reference Instruction Manual for Form Version 02/12," Version 5.0, July, 2019, accessed June 28,2020; http://www.nucc.org/images/stories/PDF/1500_claim_form_instruction_manual_2019_07 -v7.pdf

34. Dustman, R. (2016, February 16). Prolonged Services Update and Other 2016 E/M Changes. [online] assessed March 20, 2018, from https://www.aapc.com/blog/33732-prolonged-services-updates-and-other-2016-3m-changes

35. American Medical Association, *Current Procedural Terminology 2018, Standard Edition* (Chicago: American Medical Association Press, 2018).

36. "*2019 state of the states: Coverage & Reimbursement July 18, 2019.* "American Telemedicine Association, assessed June 28, 2020, https://tinyurl.com/coverageparitystates

37. *2019 state of the states: Coverage & Reimbursement July 18, 2019.* "American Telemedicine Association, assessed June 28, 2020, https://tinyurl.com/coverageparitystates or

38. Notification of Enforcement Discretion for Telehealth Remote Communications During the COVID-19 Nationwide Public Health Emergency." (See Note 20)

39. *"2019 Annual Report, California Dept. of Managed Health Care."* accessed June 28, 2020 http://dmhc.ca.gov/Portals/0/Docs/DO/2019ARFinalAccessible.pdf

40. Barstow, Scott, "The Affordable Care Act: What Counselors Should Know," The American Counseling Association, accessed June 28, 2020 https://www.counseling.org/PublicPolicy/PDF/What_counselors_should_know-the_Affordable_Care_Act_12-12.pdf

41. Estoppel", Wikipedia [online]: accessed June 28, 2020. https://en.wikipedia.org/wiki/Estoppel#Reliance-based_estoppels

42. Tran, Ann and Riemersma, Mary, "Third Party Reimbursement," *The California Therapist* (March/April, 2001, updated July 2010 by Ann Tran) accessed June 28, 2020 http://www.camft.org/COS/The_Therapist/Legal_Articles/Mary/Third_Party_Reimbursement.aspx

43. Tresca, Taryn, "Why Should Providers File Claims Electronically?" on Availity.com, posted 1/5/17; assessed June 28, 2020, https://www.availity.com/blog/2017/january/why%20should%20providers%20file%20claims%20electronically

44. CAMFT's 2017 Demographic Survey," A Snapshot of the 'Typical' California MFT, Clinical Survey," The California Association of Marriage and Family Therapists, accessed June 27, 2020, https://www.camft.org/Portals/0/PDFs/Demographic-surveys/2017/ClinicalSurvey.pdf?ver=2019-07-10-103433-993

45. Karen Rose, posting on East Bay Chapter, California Association of Marriage and Family Therapist's listserve, March 4, 2008 (used with permission).

46. Tresca, Taryn, "Why Should Providers File Claims Electronically?" on Availity.com, posted 1/5/17; assessed June 28, 2020, https://www.availity.com/blog/2017/january/why%20should%20providers%20file%20claims%20electronically

47. California HealthCare Foundation, "California Healthcare Foundation, National Consumer Health Privacy Survey 2005, " [online]; accessed January 31, 2018, http://www.chcf.org/publications/2005/11/national-consumer-health-privacy-survey-2005

48. Susan Frager, quoted in "Managed Care: Strategies for Billing Insurance and MCOs for Marital Therapy," *Psychotherapy Finances* (November 2005), p. 2.

49. Michael Brandt, "Health Care Fraud Affects Everyone," *Health Net Physician News* (Spring 2000), p. 7.

50. Tran, Ann; Jensen, David, and Riemersma, Mary, "What is Insurance Fraud?" Updated October 2017 by David Jensen, JD, CAMFT Staff Attorney; accessed June 28, 2020 https://www.camft.org/Resources/Legal-Articles/Chronological-Article-List/what-is-insurance-fraud

51. Susan Frager, LCSW, owner of PsychAdmin Partners Mental Health Billing Service, e-mail to the author, April 8, 2008 (used with permission).

52. Value Options "Treatment Record Review Results: Are you Compliant?" The Valued Provider, Spring 2006, p.6 [online]; accessed June 28, 2020 http://www.valueoptions.com/providers/News/The_Valued_Provider/2006/Spring_2006_The_Valued_Provider.pdf

53. David Jensen, J.D., attorney, phone conversation with author, March 2, 2011.

54. CAMFT's 2017 Demographic Survey," A Snapshot of the 'Typical' California MFT, Clinical Survey," The California Association of Marriage and Family Therapists, accessed June 28, 2020, https://www.camft.org/Portals/0/PDFs/Demographic-surveys/2017/ClinicalSurvey.pdf?ver=2019-07-10-103433-993

55. *"U.S. Department of Justice, Antitrust Division Manual, Chapter 2,";* assessed February 19, 2018, http://www.justice.gov/atr/public/divisionmanual/chapter2.pdf

56. Havins, Weldon, *Nevada Physician Legal Handbook*, Chapter 3 Antitrust, assessed June 28, 2020, http://www.wehavins.com/nev-physicians-legal-handbook/chapter-3-antitrust/

57. *"U.S. Department of Justice, Antitrust Division Manual, Chapter 2,";* assessed February 19, 2018, http://www.justice.gov/atr/public/divisionmanual/chapter2.pdf

APPENDIX A

State Insurance Departments

൯ ൰

The contact information below is a place to start to get information about filing complaints about insurance plans, to appeal care or claim denials, or to request Independent (or external) treatment reviews. This information is from the website of each state's Department of Insurance (accessed June 23, 2020).

Alabama Department of Insurance
http://www.aldoi.gov
334-241-4151

Alaska Division of Insurance
https://www.commerce.alaska.gov/web/ins/Consumers/Health.aspx
907-269-7900 or 1-800-467-8725

Arizona Department of Insurance
https://insurance.az.gov/hca
602-364-2499 (or 800-325-2548 in-state)

Arkansas Department of Insurance
http://insurance.arkansas.gov
800-282-9134 or 501-371-2600

California Department of Insurance
http://www.insurance.ca.gov
800-927-4357

▶ **California Department of Managed Health Care**
http://www.dmhc.ca.gov
888-466-2219

Colorado Division of Insurance
http://www.dora.state.co.us/insurance
303-894-7499
800-930-3745

State of Connecticut Insurance Department
http://www.ct.gov/cid/site/default.asp
800-203-3447 or 860-297-3900

Delaware Insurance Department
http://www.delawareinsurance.gov
302-674-7310 or 1-800-282-8611 in-state

District of Columbia Department of Insurance, Securities, and Banking
http://disb.dc.gov
202-727-8000

Florida Office of Insurance Regulation
http://www.floir.com
850-413-3140

Georgia Office of Insurance and Safety Fire Commissioner
http://www.oci.ga.gov
800-656-2298 or 404-656-2070

Hawaii Department of Insurance
http://hawaii.gov/dcca/ins/
808-586-2790

Idaho Department of Insurance
http://www.doi.idaho.gov
208-334-4250 or 800-721-3272

Illinois Department of Insurance
http://insurance.illinois.gov
866-445-5364 or 312-814-2420

Indiana Department of Insurance
http://www.in.gov/idoi
800-457-8283

Iowa Insurance Division
http://www.iid.state.ia.us/
515-281-5705

Kansas Insurance Department
http://www.ksinsurance.org/
800-432-2484 or 785-296-3071

Kentucky Department of Insurance
http://insurance.ky.gov
800-595-6053 or 502-564-3630

Louisiana Department of Insurance
http://www.ldi.la.gov
225-342-5900 or 800-259-5300 or 01

Maine Bureau of Insurance
http://www.state.me.us/pfr/insurance
800-300-5000 or 207-624-8475

Maryland Insurance Administration
http://www.mdinsurance.state.md.us/
410-468-2000 or 800-492-6116

Massachusetts Division of Insurance
http://www.mass.gov/doi
877-563-4467 or 617- 521-7794

Michigan Department of
Insurance and Financial Services
https://www.michigan.gov/difs/
877-999-6442

Minnesota Department of Health,
Managed Care Section
https://www.health.state.mn.us/facilities/i
nsurance/managedcare/index.html
651-201-5100 or 800-657-3916

Mississippi Insurance Department
http://www.mid.state.ms.us
800-562-2957 or 601-359-3569

Missouri Department of Insurance
http://insurance.mo.gov/
800-726-7390

Montana Insurance Division
http://sao.mt.gov
800-332-6148 or 406-444-2040

Nebraska Department of Insurance
http://www.doi.ne.gov
877-564-7323 (in-state only) or
402-471-2201

Nevada Division of Insurance
http://doi.state.nv.us
888-872-3234

New Hampshire Insurance Department
http://www.state.nh.us/insurance/
603-271-2261

New Jersey Department of Banking and
Insurance
http://www.state.nj.us/dobi/
800-446-7467 or 609-292-7272

New Mexico Public Regulation
Commission, Insurance Division,
Managed Healthcare Bureau
http://www.nmprc.state.nm.us
888-4-ASK-PRC

New York State Department of Health
Division of Managed Care
https://www.health.ny.gov/health_care/
managed_care/complaints/
800-206-8125 Managed Care Complaints

North Carolina Department of Insurance
http://www.ncdoi.com
855-408-1212

North Dakota Insurance Department
http://www.nd.gov/ndins/
701-328-2440

Ohio Department of Insurance,
Consumer Services Division
www.insurance.ohio.gov
800-686-1526 or 614-644-2658

Oklahoma Insurance Department
http://www.ok.gov/oid/
405-521-2828

Oregon Insurance Division
http://insurance.oregon.gov
888-877-4894 (in Oregon)

Pennsylvania Insurance Department
www.insurance.pa.gov
877-881-6388

Rhode Island Office of the Health Insurance Commissioner
http://www.ohic.ri.gov
855-747-3224 or 401-462-9517

South Carolina Department of Insurance
http://www.doi.sc.gov
803-737-6160

South Dakota Division of Insurance
http://dlr.sd.gov/reg/insurance
605-773-3563

Tennessee Department of Commerce and Insurance, Insurance Division, Consumer Insurance Services
http://www.tennessee.gov/commerce/section/insurance
800-342-4029 or 615-741-2218

Texas Department of Insurance
https://www.tdi.texas.gov
800-578-4677 or 512-676-6000

Utah Insurance Department
Health Insurance Division & Office of Consumer Health Assistance (OCHA)
http://www.insurance.utah.gov/
801-538-3800 and 800-439-3805

Vermont Department of Banking, Insurance, Securities, and Health Care Administration -- Division of Health Care Administration
https://dfr.vermont.gov/industry/insurance
800-964-1784 or 802-828-3302

Virginia Office of the Managed Care Ombudsmen
https://scc.virginia.gov/pages/Office-of-the-Managed-Care-Ombudsman
877-310-6560 option 1

Washington D.C. *(see District of Columbia)*

Washington Office of the Insurance Commissioner
http://www.insurance.wa.gov/
800-562-6900

West Virginia Offices of the Insurance Commissioner, Consumer Service Division
http://www.wvinsurance.gov/
888-879-9842 or 304-558-3386

Wisconsin Office of the Commissioner of Insurance
http://oci.wi.gov/oci_home.htm
608-266-3585; complaints 800-236-8517

Wyoming Insurance Department
http://insurance.state.wy.us
800-438-5768 or 307-777-7401

Resources

No endorsement implied, unless stated. Updated June 24, 2020

ЯО CಞЗ

MENTAL HEALTH INSURANCE CONSULTANTS

Barbara Griswold, LMFT
Author of this book. Consults with
therapists nationwide to answer insurance
questions, helping them prepare for
treatment reviews, understand audits,
fight denials. Give general practice-
business or marketing advice. Check out
her webinars on Progress Notes Writing,
CPT coding, Telehealth, and Insurance.
Billing Service Referral List, claim forms,
Subscribe to e-mail newsletter.
4010 Moorpark Ave. Suite 118
San Jose, CA 95117
(408) 985-0846
www.theInsuranceMaze.com
BarbGris@aol.com

Lynn Grodzki, LCSW
Private practice coach and author
304 Ellsworth Drive
Silver Spring, MD 20910
(301) 434-0766
www.privatepracticesuccess.com
info@privatepracticesuccess.com

Private Practice Startup
Kate Campbell and Katie Lemieux
Practice startup and marketing courses,
podcasts about practice building, legal
and ethical Paperwork Packet
754-307-7528
www.privatepracticestartup.com
Kate@theprivatepracticestartup.com

Joseph Sanok
"Practice of the Practice"
Great podcasts, coaching, classes to start
or grow your practice
www.PracticeofthePractice.com
joe@practiceofthepractice.com

GROUP PRACTICE COACHES

Group Practice Success
Joe Bavonese, Ernie Schmidt, Ken Urie
www.grouppracticesuccess.com
info@grouppracticesuccess.com

Group Practice Profits
Casey Truffo and Joe Bavonese
Coaching for group practice owners to
help reduce overwhelm and maximize
profits
www.grouppracticeprofits.com

The Group Practice Exchange
Maureen Werrbach
"Support for Group Practice Owners at
Any Stage"
https://thegrouppracticeexchange.com
hello@thegrouppracticeexchange.com

CMS-1500 BILLING FORMS

▶ *Be sure to buy latest version (at this
   writing, 02/12 version)*
▶ *Submitting claims on original red
   forms is recommended*
▶ *Get "single-sheet laser" if you use a
   printer. If you handwrite and want
   a copy, order "2-part, duplicates"*

www.theInsuranceMaze.com
Buy claim forms at author's website
www.theInsuranceMaze.com/store

www.Staples.com
1-800-333-3330
www.Staples.com

National Uniform Claim Committee
Get more detailed line-by-line details on
how to complete the claim form
https://tinyurl.com/nuccinstructions

NATIONAL PROVIDER IDENTIFIER (NPI)

National Plan and Provider Enumeration System (NPPES)
Apply for your NPI: The NPI Enumerator
P.O. Box 6059
Fargo, ND 58108-6059
(800) 465-3203
https://nppes.cms.hhs.gov/#/
customerservice@npienumerator.com

For more information about the NPI:
Centers for Medicare/Medicaid Services
7500 Security Boulevard
Baltimore, MD 21244
(800) 465-3203
https://tinyurl.com/NPIinfo

PROGRESS NOTES / CHARTS

"What Should Be In Your Client Charts –
And Probably Isn't: Writing Great
Progress Notes and Treatment Plans"
Pre-Recorded Webinar with Barbara
Griswold, LMFT, author of this book.
Covers what licensing boards, ethics
committees, and insurance plans want in
your notes. Sample notes and templates.
www.theinsurancemaze.com/store

Practice Forms Packet
A packet of 15 essential forms for
therapists.
created by Barbara Griswold
www.theinsurancemaze.com/formspacket

Also, Barbara is available for
consultations about your notes and
treatment plans, and helps you respond
to records requests and treatment reviews
Barbara Griswold, LMFT
408-985-0846

Maelisa Hall, PhD
QA Prep
Helps mental health professionals with
paperwork, notes, treatment plan Helps
you catch up on months of unwritten
notes
www.qaprep.com
drmaelisahall@gmail.com

TELEHEALTH / ONLINE THERAPY

The Telebehavioral Health Institute
Marlene Maheu, Ph.D., Exec. Director
Consultations, online therapy trainings;
support community, good e-news.
619-255-2788
https://telehealth.org
Contact: https://telehealth.org/contact

American Telemedicine Association
901 N. Glebe Road, Ste 850
Arlington, VA 22203
http://www.americantelemed.org
703-373-9600
info@americantelemed.org

Person-Centered Tech
Working with therapists, these are the
experts on all things related to
technology and therapy, including HIPAA
and telehealth. Individual consultations,
podcasts, training. Great e-newsletter.
P.O. Box 42494
Portland, OR 97242
www.personcenteredtech.com
info@personcenteredtech.com

Telehealth consent
see Barbara's Practice Forms Packet
www.theinsurancemaze.com/formspacket

INSURANCE COMPANY LISTS

Many professional associations have a list
of plans that operate in your state and
their contact information

State Departments of Insurance may have
such lists on websites (see Page 129)

Barbara Griswold, MFT
Sells list of plans that operate in
California, with mailing labels to use for
applications: not available on website
barbgris@aol.com
408-985-0846

Billing Service List
Compiled by author Barbara Griswold
List of over 38 mental health billing
services nationwide, including fees,
services offered, reviews from therapists,
and suggested interview questions for
hiring a biller.
www.theInsuranceMaze.com/Store
BarbGris@aol.com

Tame Your Practice
Rob Reinhardt
Reviews practice management software
and electronic health records. Will help
you choose the right one for your
practice. Consultations.
602 E. Academy St. Suite 205
Fuquay-Varina, NC 27526
(919) 578 8263
rob@tameyourpractice.com
https://tameyourpractice.com

Office Ally
Offers submission of claims to health
plans, FREE online practice billing system
(PracticeMate)
PO Box 872020, Vancouver, WA 98687
(360) 975-7000
www.officeally.com
info@officeally.com

SimplePractice
Recommended practice management
program: with telehealth services, notes,
forms, electronic billing, client portal; has
comparisons to other top programs
www.simplepractice.com

Capterra
Maintains list of top mental health
software products, with reviews and
details of what each can do. Use filters to
search for software that meets your needs
1201 Wilson Blvd. 9th Floor
Arlington, VA. 22209
www.capterra.com/mental-health-
software
(855) 467-6389
info@capterra.com

ParityTrack
View Legislation, File Complaints, View
State Parity Implementation Survey
https://www.paritytrack.org

National Alliance on Mental Illness
3803 N. Fairfax Dr., Suite 100
Arlington, VA 22203
(800) 950-6264
www.nami.org

Mental Health America
500 Montgomery Street, Suite 820
Alexandria, VA 22314
(800) 969-6642 or (703) 684-7722
www.nmha.org (search "parity")

Parity Implementation Coalition
(866)882-6227
http://parityispersonal.org/
info@parityispersonal.org

"CPT Coding Tips: Maximize
Reimbursement and Avoid Denials"
Pre-recorded webinar presented by
author Barbara Griswold, MFT; avoid
common mistakes, use more codes to
increase reimbursement
www.theInsuranceMaze.com/store
(408) 985.0846
barbgris@aol.com

Current Procedural Terminology Codes
American Medical Association Bookstore
Orders: PO Box 74008935
Chicago, IL 60674-8935
(800) 621-8335
https://commerce.ama-
assn.org/store/?node_id=nn1402

Place of Service Codes (POS)
Center for Medicare/Medicaid Services
http://tinyurl.com/placeofservice

DIAGNOSIS CODES

DSM-5 Diagnostic and Statistical Manual of Mental Disorders
Contains psychiatric diagnoses and criteria
American Psychiatric Publishing
800 Maine Avenue, SW, Suite 900
Washington DC 20024
800-368-5777
https://www.appi.org/Products/dsm

www.icd10data.com
free online website where you can find and check diagnosis codes
Note: Type in name of diagnosis or DSM or ICD code in search bar; in results listing, look for green triangle next to a code to tell you it is OK to use, red triangle tells you it is not

THE AFFORDABLE CARE ACT, AND RESOURCES FOR FINDING INSURANCE

HealthCare.gov
Open to anyone, but particularly great for folks who don't have employer-sponsored insurance, offers marketplace insurance options to the uninsured.
(800) 318-2596 (24 hours, 7 days/week)
www.healthcare.gov

Healthcare.gov Insurance Plan Finder
Part of HealthCare.org, this web tool will help you find private insurance or public program options outside the marketplace plans, for individuals, families, and small businesses
http://finder.healthcare.gov/

HIPAA RESOURCES

Person-Centered Tech
Working with therapists, these are the experts on all things related to technology and therapy, including HIPAA and telehealth. Individual consultations, podcasts, training. Great e-newsletter.
P.O. Box 42494
Portland, OR 97242
www.personcenteredtech.com
info@personcenteredtech.com

U.S. Dept of Health and Human Services
200 Independence Ave. SW
Washington, DC, 20201
(800) 368-1019
www.hhs.gov/ocr/hipaa

Center for Medicare/Medicaid Services
7500 Security Boulevard
Baltimore, MD 21244
https://tinyurl.com/cmsHIPAA

EMPLOYER IDENTIFICATION NUMBERS

Internal Revenue Service
When *switching from Social Security Number to EIN, submit IRS Form W-9 to each plan, check to see if they got it.*
http://tinyurl.com/getyourEIN or
www.irs.gov (search EIN)

NO Endorsement or recommendation of any of these resources is implied, unless stated. Author cannot be held liable for the quality of service provided by any individual or agency on this list.
Updated June 2020 but all information is subject to change.

Glossary

ৠ ৣ

Account: An agreement an insurance company may have with an employer, union, or government, (ex. "CureQuick offers their Premier HMO $15 Copayment plan to the Microsoft Employer account.") A care management team at the insurance company may be devoted to one account or employer group.

Ad hoc agreement: See Single case agreement.

Appeal: A process available to clients, their family members, their treating providers, or their representatives to request reconsideration of a previous denial of claim reimbursement, or previous denied request for a covered service or authorization for service (see Sample Appeal Letter, Page 84).

Audit: A review of a therapist's file on a particular client or group of clients by the health plan in order to assure quality of care and to be sure the therapist is following insurance procedures.

Authorization: See Pre-authorization

Balance-billing: This is when a provider charges the client the difference between the provider's full fee and the insurance plan rate. Balance billing is forbidden for network providers -- they may not bill clients for this difference.

Behavioral health care: Services for the assessment and treatment of mental health and/or substance abuse issues.

Benefit year: The coverage period, usually 12 months long, that is used for administration of a health benefits plan. Clients, for example, may have benefits for 20 sessions from January 1 through December 31 of any year, or they may have 20 sessions between July 1 of one year and June 30 of the next year.

Benefits: The portion of costs of services paid by a health plan. If the plan pays the remainder of a bill after an office copayment is made, the amount the plan paid is the benefit.

Care manager: See Case manager

Carrier: An insurance company is often referred to as the insurance carrier.

Carve-out: When a health insurance company has decided not to manage the mental health benefits for their members, they may instead "carved out" their mental health benefits, by signing a contract with another company to handle the mental health case management and/or claims payment.

Case manager: Case managers work for the insurance company, reviewing clients' care to make sure it is delivered in the most cost-effective manner. They authorize treatment requests and make network referrals when needed. Also called care managers.

CEAP: see Certified Employee Assistance Provider

Certification: See Precertification

Certified Employee Assistance Provider (CEAP): A health care professional who has gone through the additional training classes required to become a Certified Employee Assistance Provider.

CHAMPUS (Civilian Health and Medical Program of the Uniformed Services): A medical benefits program provided by the federal government.

Claim: A request for payment made to the health insurance plan from the client or the treating provider.

CMS-1500 (Centers for Medicare and Medicaid Services Form 1500): Formerly known as the HCFA-1500, this is a claim form that is accepted by most private and federal health insurance plans.

COBRA (Consolidated Omnibus Budget Reconciliation Act): A federal statute that requires employers to continue to offer coverage to employees and dependents who would otherwise have lost their insurance coverage for reasons specified in the statute (for example, loss of a job, disability, divorce, loss of dependent child status, employee death, etc.). They are given the opportunity to purchase or take over payment of the premiums for the same health benefits the employer provides to its remaining employees. Continuation of coverage is limited (usually 18 months for employees and dependents who would otherwise lose coverage due to loss of employment or work hour reduction, 29 months for disability-related events, or 36 months for dependents who would lose coverage for other reasons).

Co-insurance: Clients usually have a co-insurance or copayment. A co-insurance is the percentage of the provider's fee that a client is responsible to pay (after his or her deductible has been met, if any). For example, if the insurance plan pays 80 percent of the claim, the client's co-insurance is 20 percent.

Continuity of care: These are actions that a provider takes to help a client make a smooth transition from or to another mental health provider.

Contract (subscriber's): A legal agreement between a member (the client or a family member) and the insurance plan that describes the benefits and limitations of the coverage.

Contract (provider's): A legal agreement between an individual treating provider and the insurance plan outlining the terms of their agreement to provide services to covered members.

Contracted rate, or contracted fee: The fee the insurance company will pay for a session, as outlined in the network provider contract. This is usually a discounted fee from the provider's usual full fee.

Coordination of benefits (COB): When a client has two or more insurance plans, the plans will coordinate the payment of the claim to see which plan is primary, to prevent overpayment/duplication.

Copayment (copay): Most plans have a copayment or coinsurance. If there is a copayment, this is the fixed, flat fee per visit that a client must pay for eligible expenses, after any deductible is met. The health insurance company pays the rest, up to the contracted rate.

Coverage: The benefits provided by the insurance plan – what services and diagnoses are covered, at what frequency, and at what rate.

Covered services: Those procedures the insurance company agrees to pay under the member's benefit contract. Most health insurance plans have limitations on their coverage.

CPT codes: The physician's Current Procedural Terminology codes, published by the American Medical Association, were developed to provide a universal language to describe medical and diagnostic services provided by health care providers.

Credentialing: A process used by an insurance company in which a health care provider's credentials are reviewed and matched against the credentials required to participate in the provider network.

Date of service (DOS): The date of the service or session that was provided to the client.

Deductible: The dollar amount that a client must pay yearly for eligible health services before his health plan begins paying. For example, a client with a $200 deductible will have to pay the first $200 of medical bills each year before insurance begins to cover the expenses. Not all plans have deductibles. During the deductible period, network providers should charge clients their contracted amount and continue to submit claims; only the contracted amount will be credited toward the deductible.

Dependent: A person eligible for coverage under an employee benefits plan because of that person's relationship to an employee, including spouses, children, and adopted children.

Dispute: Also known as an appeal. A provider's written notice to the insurance company challenging, appealing, or requesting reconsideration of a claim that has been denied, adjusted, or contested, or disputing a request for reimbursement of an overpayment of a claim.

Dispute resolution: The process that each insurance plan has set up for handling and settling disputes.

DOS: See Date of service

Double (or duplicate) coverage: When a client has coverage under more than one health benefits plan (e.g., he is covered by insurance through both his employer and his wife's employer, or when a couple you are seeing both have their own plans).

DSM: *The Diagnostic and Statistical Manual of Mental Disorders*, published by the American Psychiatric Association, provides a common language and standard criteria for the diagnosis and classification of mental disorders.

EAP: See Employee Assistance Program, or employee assistance provider/professional.

EIN (Employer Identification Number): This is a type of Tax Identification Number (TIN) that any business (including therapists in private practice) can obtain from the Internal Revenue Service. The EIN can be used on claims and invoices in place of your Social Security Number.

Effective date: The date on which the client's coverage began under the health benefits plan.

Eligible services: Services are considered eligible or ineligible for coverage by the health benefits plan depending on the plan's provisions.

Employee assistance professional/provider: A clinician who has contracted with an Employee Assistance Program (EAP) to provide counseling services which are free to the employee or dependent (see also "Employee Assistance Program").

Employee Assistance Program (EAP): An EAP is an assessment, referral and short-term counseling program that is paid for by some employers and is available for free to their employees and dependents as an employee benefit. An employer may hire EAP professionals that work onsite at the company, or may contract with clinicians in the community.

Employee Retirement Income Security Act (ERISA): A federal law that applies to retirement programs and to employee welfare benefit programs established or maintained by employers and unions. Because these plans are governed by ERISA, which is federal law, the federal law pre-empts state law, and thus self-insured benefit plans can avoid certain state mandates.

Employer Identification Number: see EIN

Enrollee: An individual who is enrolled and eligible for coverage under a health plan.

EOB: See Explanation of Benefits.

EPO (exclusive provider organization): A specific type of health plan similar to a PPO, except that the client does not have the option of choosing an out-of-network provider for reimbursable services. Plan members can visit specialists without a referral, and don't need to choose a primary care physician for coverage.

ERISA: See Employee Retirement Income Security Act

Exclusions: Specific conditions or services that are not covered under the plan's benefit agreement.

Exclusive provider organization: See EPO

Explanation of Benefits (EOB): Once a claim is made for services, an EOB is the statement provided by the health plan that accompanies the reimbursement check, and explains how the claim was processed. It may include the portion of the charges that went to satisfy the client's deductible or co-insurance, and any other adjustments made before it was paid. Or it may explain why no payment was made. A copy of the EOB goes to both the insured and the provider.

Fee-for-service plans: A healthcare plan in which providers receive payment based on their billed charges for each service provided without treatment review or authorization. These plans are not considered "managed care," and allow visits to any healthcare professional. See Indemnity plans.

Flexible spending account (FSA): An employer-sponsored tax-advantaged savings account that clients may use to pay medical and dependent care expenses from pre-tax dollars. Clients must say in advance how much they want to put in the account each year, and if not spent by year-end, it is lost.

HCFA-1500: The old name for the CMS-1500 claim form. See CMS-1500.

Health Insurance Portability and Accountability Act: see HIPAA

Health maintenance organization: See HMO

Health reimbursement account (HRA): These are tax-exempt accounts that many employers have paid into that employees may use specifically for the payment of health care expenses. Clients control the investments they make, the amount they deposit, and what expenses they pay.

Health savings account (HSA): These are tax-exempt accounts that many clients (and often their employers) have paid into that employees may use for the payment of health care expenses. Clients control the investments they make, the amount they deposit, and what expenses they pay. They are also required to have a high deductible health plan.

HIPAA (Health Insurance Portability and Accountability Act): This law addresses health insurance portability, and is designed to protect health insurance coverage for workers and their families when they change or lose their jobs. It is also aimed at reducing the administrative costs of providing health care through standardization, and includes requirements to protect the privacy of clients' health information. Health plans and many providers who transmit confidential health information electronically are required to follow the requirements of HIPAA.

HMO (health maintenance organization): A health plan that typically offers broader preventive coverage and lower out-of-pocket expenses for its members. Plan members are required to have a primary care physician, who coordinates care, and his/her referral may be required to see specialists. There is typically no annual deductible, and copayments are usually low. However, coverage is not available for out-of-network providers, except for emergency care.

HRA: See Health reimbursement arrangement

HSA: See Health savings account

ICD (International Classification of Diseases): Medical and psychiatric diagnostic codes maintained by the World Health Organization, and now required by most health insurers on claim forms.

Indemnity plan: A type of health benefits plan under which the covered person pays an annual deductible, and then the health benefit plan pays a percentage of covered charges. No primary care physician referral is required, no referrals are required for specialists, and there are no provider networks. The provider controls the type of treatment, length of treatment, and fee charged. Also called a fee-for-service plan.

Insured: The individual who is enrolled and eligible for coverage under a health plan.

Invoice: Also known as a statement or superbill (see sample invoice Page 145). A list of charges and payments made for healthcare services provided. Out-of-network providers may give these to a client to submit to their insurance plan for reimbursement (network providers must bill for clients).

Legacy Identifiers: These are provider identification numbers other than the National Provider Identifier (NPI) used by a health plan to identify a provider. Examples include Provider Identification Numbers (PINS), Unique Physician Identification Numbers (UPINs) and state license numbers. Legacy Identifiers may still be accepted on claim forms by some insurance plans if a provider is not a HIPAA Covered Entity, in which case the provider is required to use a NPI

Lifetime maximum/limit: The cap placed on the benefits paid under an insurance policy during a client's lifetime. Due to the Affordable Care Act, most plans no longer have these limits.

Managed care: A system of health care delivery that is designed to manage the cost, use and quality of the health care, and typically offers financial incentives for clients to use the providers who belong to the plan's provider network. Managed care may include pretreatment authorization, session limits, utilization review, and provider discounts. Examples include HMO, PPO, EPO, and POS plans.

Medical necessity: The health plan's determination that there is a medical need for treatment, that the course of treatment is the most appropriate for the symptoms the client is experiencing, is provided within generally accepted standards of practice, and is not rendered primarily for the convenience of the client or provider.

Medical savings account (MSA): See Health savings account

Member: The individual or dependent who is enrolled in and eligible for coverage under a health plan.

MH/SA: An abbreviation used by insurers to refer to Mental Health and Substance Abuse benefits. Do not confuse with MHSA, which can mean "Mental Health Service Administrators" indicating there may be a carve-out of mental health benefits to another plan, a "mental health service administrator."

National Provider Identifier (NPI): As part of HIPAA laws, The Centers for Medicare and Medicaid Services (CMS) will be assigning all HIPAA providers ("covered entities") unique provider identification numbers to use when billing and communicating with all private and government health plans.

Network: A group of health care providers under contract with an insurance company. They may agree to accept discounts, file claims, and permit their treatment to be reviewed.

Network provider: Any health care provider who has entered into an agreement with an insurance plan, and thus belongs to the insurance plan's network of providers. Choosing a network provider gives the member the advantage of discounted fees, having claims filed on their behalf, and often better coverage by the health plan. Also called a participating provider.

NPI: see National Provider Identifier

Open enrollment: A period when eligible persons can enroll in a new health benefit plan for the next benefit year.

Out-of-network provider: Any health care provider that does not belong to the insurance plan's network. Many insurance plans (including PPO and POS plans) cover visits to out-of-network providers, but often at a lower reimbursement rate.

Out-of-pocket expenses: Copayments, deductibles, or fees paid by clients for health services.

Out-of-pocket maximum: The out of pocket sum a client will be required to pay per year before the plan begins to pay 100 percent of covered health expenses. This does not include the payment of regular premiums. In some plans, the client may still have to pay copayments.

Panel: The network of providers who have contracted with a health care plan to provide services to the insurance members or enrollees. Also known as the provider network.

Parity: State or federal laws which require insurance companies to grant some measure of equality between the benefits they provide for mental health and medical visits.

Participant: A person who is eligible to receive benefits under a health benefits plan. This may refer to the employee, spouse, or other dependents.

Participating provider: Any health care provider that has entered into an agreement with an insurance plan, and thus belongs to the insurance plan's network of providers. Choosing a participating provider (network provider) gives the member the advantage of discounted fees, not having to file their own claims, and often a higher level of coverage by the health plan. Also called a network provider.

Pass-through: Some health plans allow a certain number of visits with a provider before authorization for treatment is needed. These are sometimes called "pass-through sessions."

Payer: An insurance company, self-funded employer, union or employer trust, insurance plan, state or federal government agency which has entered into a contractual arrangement to pay for health services for a client or member.

PCP: See Primary care physician

Pended claim: A claim that has been delayed because it requires additional information before it can be processed. This often involves waiting for information about whether the client has a second insurance plan covering him or her.

Place-of-service code: See POS code

Plan: An employee benefits arrangement offered by an insurance company so that health care services are provided to covered members or enrollees in the plan.

Point-of-service plan: See POS plan.

Policyholder: The individual to whom an insurance contract is issued, usually the employee in an employer-sponsored health plan. Also called the subscriber.

Portability: The ability for an individual to transfer from one health insurance plan to another (including after a change of job status, or change of plans offered by the employer) and still be covered.

POS (Place-of-service) code: This code, placed on a claim form, informs insurance companies where the treatment took place.

POS (point-of-service) plan: A health plan allowing members to choose to receive services from participating or non-participating providers. Some plans afford clients the choice to see the plan's HMO providers, PPO providers, or any licensed provider, and their coverage level will vary accordingly. If the client chooses an out-of-network provider, out-of-pocket expenses may be higher.

PPO (preferred provider organization): A type of insurance health plan with a network of providers. The health plan has contracted with these providers to provide services at a discounted fee. Clients can visit providers both in and out of the network, but will pay a higher portion of the cost for an out-of-network provider. Network providers must file claims on the client's behalf. Members don't need to choose a primary care physician for coverage, and can visit specialists without a referral.

Pre-authorization: The process of obtaining approval from the health plan for sessions or hospital admission prior to the start of treatment.

Pre-certification: See Pre-authorization.

Pre-existing condition: A health condition (other than pregnancy) that was diagnosed or treated within six months prior to the client's enrollment in a new health plan (or a condition for which a reasonable person would have sought medical advice). Prior to the Affordable Care Act, many insurance plans would not cover pre-existing conditions, or would only cover them after a waiting period. Plans that still can exclude pre-existing conditions are rare.

Preferred provider organization plan: See PPO

Premium: The upfront amount the client or employer pays monthly or yearly in exchange for health insurance coverage.

Primary care physician (PCP): A client's main physician, usually a family or general practitioner, internist (or for children, pediatrician), who provides a broad range of routine medical services and refers clients to specialists, hospitals, and other providers as needed. Some health plans require that the client has a PCP, and may require a PCP's referral to obtain services from other providers.

Prior authorization: See Pre-authorization.

Private-pay Agreement: An agreement between client and therapist where the client agrees to pay for services out of pocket (see sample on Page 149).

Provider: A licensed health care facility, program, agency, physician, or other health professional that delivers health care services.

Provider network: A panel of providers contracted by a health plan to deliver medical services to the enrollees. The providers usually agree to accept a fee discount, and to file claims on behalf of the client. Also called a provider panel.

Provider panel: See Provider network

Quality assurance: The steps taken by a health plan to ensure quality of care, including provider credentialing, auditing, treatment reviews, and other monitoring of provider care.

Recredentialing: A process used by an insurance company in which a network provider's information is updated and credentials are again reviewed and matched against the qualifications required to participate in the provider network. This is done at regular intervals (ex. every 1-3 years).

Retro-authorization: An authorization for treatment given by an insurance company after the date of service has already passed.

SED (serious emotional disturbance): In certain state parity laws, children are afforded mental health coverage which is equal to that of medical coverage if they have diagnoses which meet the criteria in the state's parity law for "serious emotional disturbance."

Self-funded/self-insured plan: This is a type of health plan that is self-funded by the employer. Some plans contract with insurance carriers for claims processing and other administrative services, others may be self-administered. With self-funded plans, federal law (instead of state law) applies, and the benefits may be different from non-self-funded insurance plans.

Serious Emotional Disturbance: See SED

Severe mental illness (SMI): This term is used in some state parity laws. In these state laws, only clients with a diagnosis that qualifies as a "severe mental illness" may be entitled to coverage that is equal to the coverage the plan offers for medical claims. Also known as "parity diagnoses."

Single case agreement: When an appropriate provider cannot be found who is available to provide services within a reasonable distance from the client and within the client's provider network, or when no network providers have the specialized training or expertise a client needs, a health plan may often be compelled to contract with an out-of-network provider to act as a network provider for this one case. Also known as an ad hoc agreement. See also "transition of care agreements."

SMI : See Severe mental illness.

Split-year claims: Claims that have charges from two or more years on the form (not recommended).

Statement: *See Invoice or Superbill.*

Subscriber: The holder of the insurance – the primary insured person who is enrolled and eligible for coverage under a health plan.

Superbill: A list of charges and payments made for healthcare services provided. This may be given to a client to submit to their insurance plan for reimbursement. Also known as a statement or invoice.

Telehealth: Providing treatment, education, and administration of health services over a distance. While each state defines telehealth differently, it typically involves the application of both video and audio technologies in synchronous (real-time "live") treatment delivery. Some states include telephone in their definition, though this is rarely covered by insurance

Telemedicine: See telehealth.

Third-party administrator (TPA): An individual or firm hired by the employer to handle claims processing, pay providers, and manage other functions related to health insurance.

Third-party payer: Any payer for health care services other than the client. Examples include insurance companies and the federal government.

Transitional benefits/plans: When an employer changes insurance carriers, transition plans enable clients already in treatment to transition to a provider in the new network. They give the client and his current provider a specific number of days to contact the insurance company in order to discuss the client's treatment plan and to obtain authorization to continue treatment at the network benefit level for a specified period of time, or to transition to a professional in the new network.

TRICARE: The Defense Department's insurance plan for military dependents and retirees.

Usual, customary and reasonable (UCR) charges: The amount that the insurance company has determined is reasonable for a particular service, taking into account the providers degree, licensure, and the usual fees for similar providers in your geographical area. The UCR is the maximum the plan will pay for any service. Since network providers have contracted rates, this applies only to out-of- network providers.

Utilization: Measurement of the use of health insurance by employees of an insured employer, stated in terms of the average number of claims per employee.

Utilization management/review (UM/UR): The processes by which an insurance plan reviews a provider's treatment requests to determine whether care decisions are appropriate and to make reimbursement decisions, with a view to contain costs and monitor quality of care. This review may take place before, during, or after services have been rendered.

Sample Treatment Agreement

Please initial in each box on the left after reading the text to the right:

INITIAL BELOW	
	FEES: The fee per 50-minute session is $_____ (except for the first session, which is $_____). This is due at the time of our session in cash or check, unless I am billing your insurance, in which case you must pay your copayment and/or deductible at the session.
	CANCELLATION: Sessions are by appointment only. While I hate charging for missed sessions, I do reserve that time for you. Therefore, you will be charged $_____ (not just a copayment) for missed sessions or for those cancelled without 24-hour notice, except in medical emergency. Insurance will not pay for missed sessions. Since your time is also valuable, if I forget a session, you get one session free.
	INSURANCE: **If I am a provider with your plan:** I will submit claims for you, but at our session you must pay any copayment or co-insurance. There may be a deductible (an amount you need to pay out of pocket) before your plan begins paying. If insurance does not pay as expected, you remain responsible for the balance. You have the right to waive using insurance coverage, if desired. **If I am NOT a provider for your plan:** You will pay me in full at the session. I can give you an invoice if you wish to seek reimbursement, if your health plan covers providers who are not in their network.
	SECONDARY INSURANCE: It is your responsibility to tell me about all possible insurance plans that might cover my services (ex. if you have Medicare in addition to a secondary policy, or coverage through your work and a family member's work). If you do not, you may be responsible in full if claims are denied.
	DIAGNOSIS: If you use insurance I will be required to provide a diagnosis on invoices and claims, and coverage may be limited to certain conditions that are covered by your plan.
	LIMITS OF MEDICAL COVERAGE: Even if you have insurance coverage for unlimited sessions, health plans may review treatment for medical necessity, limit length of treatment or frequency of sessions, and request treatment notes. While I may check coverage for you, you are responsible for verifying and understanding the limits of your coverage. Although I am happy to assist your efforts in obtaining insurance reimbursement, I am unable to guarantee whether your health plan will provide payment for the services provided.
	CONFIDENTIALITY: What you say in therapy, your records, and your attendance are all confidential. Exceptions include when your records are subpoenaed for legal reasons, when reporting is required or allowed by law (ex. suspected child abuse or neglect, extreme danger to self, suspected elder abuse, or danger to others), when you give written permission to release information, and other exceptions outlined in my *Notice of Privacy Practices.*
	IN AN EMERGENCY: Contact me via e-mail and voicemail, then call my 24-hour answering service at XXX-XX-XXXX. Tell them it is an emergency; the service will try to reach me or a licensed therapist. You may also go to the emergency room or dial 911
	E-MAIL: I use e-mail to arrange appointments. Please do not e-mail me information related to your therapy, as e-mail is not completely confidential. Important issues should be reserved for sessions. Be aware that e-mails become part of your legal record.
	SOCIAL MEDIA: I do not accept friend requests or contact requests from clients on social networking sites (Facebook, LinkedIn, etc.) out of concern for your confidentiality and my privacy. It may also blur the boundaries of our therapy relationship. *(continued)*

INITIAL BELOW	*(Treatment Agreement, continued from previous page)*
	REFERRALS/GROUP: A referral to another provider may become necessary if it becomes clear in my opinion that your issues would be better treated by a professional with different expertise. It is unethical for me to practice beyond the level of my competence, education, training, or experience. I am not responsible for the care received from professionals to whom I refer you. Agreements made between you and I do not involve other professionals in the office suite, who each operate independent solo practices, and are not part of a group.
	ENDINGS: If you are unhappy with any aspect of therapy, I ask that you talk to me to see if we can work it out. Of course, you may end therapy at any time, and I am happy to assist with referrals. It is my ethical duty to provide therapy only when I feel you are actively participating and benefiting from the sessions. I may end treatment if there have been repeated no-shows, late-cancellations or other treatment interruptions.
	PATIENT RIGHTS: You have the right to ask questions about your treatment or refuse to participate in treatment. This office does not discriminate in the delivery of health care services based on race, ethnicity, national origin, citizenship or immigration status, religion, gender, gender identity, age, mental or physical disability, medical condition, sexual orientation, medical history, evidence of insurability, or source of payment.
	COMPLAINTS: The _____ (licensing board name) receives and responds to complaints regarding services provided within the scope of practice of _____ (your license). You may contact the board online at _____, or by calling _____.
	PRIVACY PRACTICES: By initialing here and signing below, you are acknowledging receipt of my *Notices of Privacy Practices*. My *Notice of Privacy Practices* provides information about how I may use and disclose your private health information. I encourage you to read it in full. My *Notice of Privacy* Practices is subject to change. If I change my Notice, I will give you a revised Notice. If you have left treatment, you may obtain the revised notice from me at the above address and phone number.

PLEASE SIGN IF USING YOUR INSURANCE OR EMPLOYEE ASSISTANCE PROGRAM:

"I authorize the release of any information necessary (Including notes, treatment summaries and diagnosis) to process insurance or Employee Assistance claims, to prove medical necessity for treatment, to request additional sessions, or to comply with treatment reviews or mandated administrative chart reviews from the insurance plan."

(Sign here) :**X** _____

If second client, sign here: **X** _____

"I authorize payment of benefits to therapist: (Sign here): **X** _____

By signing below, I acknowledge that I have read and understand the above rights and policies.

X_____ **X**_____ **X**_____

Signature   Printed Name   Date

X_____ **X**_____ **X**_____

Signature, second client (if applicable)   Printed Name, second client (if applicable)   Date

This form is available in my Practice Forms Packet: visit www.theinsurancemaze.com/store for info

Sample Invoice/Superbill

BARBARA GRISWOLD, LMFT

4010 MOORPARK AVE #118, SAN JOSE, CA 95117
TEL 408-985-0846   **EMAIL** BARBGRIS@AOL.COM

DATE OF INVOICE: _____

Client:	Birthdate: / /
SSN or Plan ID:	Group # :
Responsible Party (if other):	Resp. Party Birthdate: / /

DIAGNOSIS CODE(S):_____

Date	Place of Service Code	CPT Code	Modifier	Service Description	Charges	Credits

Common CPT Procedure Codes

- 90791 Diagnostic interview assessment
- 90832 Psychotherapy 30 min. (16 - 35 min)
- 90834 Psychotherapy 45 min. (37-52 min)
- 90837 Psychotherapy 60 min. (over 52 min)
- 90846 Couples/ Family w/o client (50 min)
- 90847 Couples / family therapy w/ct (50 min)
- 90853 Group (other than multiple-family)
- Phone or video session: Usually use Place of Service code 02 and modifier 95 or GT

Previous Balance	$
New Charges	$
New Credits	$
Current balance	$

PLEASE REIMBURSE:
____ **CLIENT**
____ **THERAPIST**
____ **OTHER:**_____

_____

SIGNATURE: BARBARA GRISWOLD, MFT (MFC27210)
TAX ID: XXX-XX-XXXX **NPI:** XXXXXXXXXX

This form is available in my Practice Forms Packet: visit www.theinsurancemaze.com/store for info

APPENDIX F

Sample Service Record

Client Name:	Jack Klutz		Diagnosis:	F43.23		Copay: $15.00

# Authorized: 8 Start: 7/1/20 Expires:7/1/21 Auth#: 1005678	Contract rate: $95 intake/couples; ind. $85

Sessions Authorized:___ Start:_____ Expires:_____ Auth#:_____	Deduct: $1500 Used? $1500

Sessions Authorized:___ Start:_____ Expires:_____ Auth#:_____

Service Date	Ses #	Client Seen	Service Description	Fee (or Contract rate)	Credits	Ct. Copay Owed	Ct. Owes Total	Ins. Owes For Ses.	Ins. Owes Total	Did Ins. Pay ?
7/1/2020	1 of 8	Jack	Intake	$95.00	$15.00	$15.00	$0.00	$80.00	$80.00	√
7/8/2020	2 of 8	Jack	Individual Ses.	$85.00	$15.00	$15.00	$0.00	$70.00	$150.00	√
7/20/2020	3 of 8	Jack & Jill	Couples Ses.	$95.00	$15.00	$15.00	$0.00	$80.00	$230.00	√
7/30/2020	4 of 8	Jack	Indiv. Video	$85.00	$15.00	$15.00	$0.00	$70.00	$300.00	√
8/1/2020	—	—	Bill for july sessions	—	—	—	$0.00	—	$300.00	—
8/7/2020	—	—	Ins. Pd. For 7/1 - 7/30	—	$300.00	—	$0.00	—	$0.00	—

This form is available in my Practice Forms Packet: visit www.theinsurancemaze.com/store for info

Sample Private-Pay Agreement

I, _____ (client name), am signing this to indicate that I am seeking treatment with _____ (provider name) and to attest that I understand my treatment, starting on _____ (date), will not be covered by insurance because:

_____ I am not aware of any insurance coverage for the services I am seeking. *If it turns out that I did have coverage, I waive any right to be reimbursed by my insurance for services that have been provided.*

_____ I choose not to use my insurance coverage. *I understand that I waive my right to be reimbursed by my insurance plan for services that have already been provided.*

_____ I have been notified by my provider or health plan that therapy will not be covered by my plan because it is not a covered benefit under my benefit plan, or does not meet the plan's medical necessity standards

_____ My benefits for this service have been exhausted or terminated as of _____(date)

_____ While some of the treatment I desire is covered by my insurance plan, some is not, and I am willing to pay for the non-covered treatment (ex. more frequent sessions, phone or video sessions).

_____ Extended sessions: I am aware that my therapist is able to bill my insurance plan only for one 45- or 60-minute session per day. If I desire additional time, I understand it is my responsibility to pay copayments and/or deductibles for this session PLUS the cost for any additional time I desire. Additional time will not be billed to the insurance plan, but I understand I will be given the benefit of the insurance discount rate. If the therapist is NOT a provider for my plan, I understand I will be expected to pay in full for the extended session. However, if I request an invoice to seek reimbursement from my health plan, I may be given an invoice that reflects only the first 45 (or 60) minutes of the session, depending on plan.

Other:_____

If the result of a decision by my plan, I have been informed of my appeal options at my plan and through my State Department of Insurance or Department of Managed Health Care. I have elected not to appeal, or am in the process of appealing. In the meantime/instead, I choose to continue treatment and pay out of pocket, understanding I will not be reimbursed by my plan unless successful on appeal.

I have chosen to begin/continue treatment with my provider on a self-pay basis starting _____(date), which is no earlier than the date I have signed this form. I agree that the provider may collect charges for the proposed services at the rates outlined below:

Description of Service to be Provided	Cost

I understand that insurance plan maximums that apply to medically necessary covered services will not apply and will not limit the amount I may become obligated to pay for the proposed services. I understand that I have a right to a copy of this form. This consent is subject to revocation at any time except to the extent that action has been already taken in reliance thereon. *I understand that in signing this I waive any future right to be reimbursed by my insurance plan for services that have already been provided.* By signing this agreement, I know that I am creating a binding contract that is legally enforceable against me by the provider.

Signature of client _____ Date:_____

Signature of therapist or witness _____ Date:_____

This form is available in my Practice Forms Packet: visit www.theinsurancemaze.com/store for info

Index

ಙ ಛ